AS/A-LEVEL

Geography

Michael Raw

ESSENTIAL WORD
DICTIONARY

840847

Philip Allan Updates
Market Place
Deddington
Oxfordshire
OX15 0SE

Tel: 01869 338652
Fax: 01869 337590
e-mail: sales@philipallan.co.uk
www.philipallan.co.uk

© Philip Allan Updates 2000

ISBN 0 86003 374 0

Printed by Raithby, Lawrence & Co Ltd, Leicester

P00244

Introduction

Accurate knowledge and understanding of technical terms is a particular challenge in geography. That is because geography, in its attempt to explain the physical and human environment, depends heavily on other disciplines. As a result, you need to be familiar not only with geographical terms but also with others drawn from subjects as diverse as economics, ecology, geology, meteorology and sociology.

This dictionary contains most of the essential words and terms you are likely to need in your AS and A-level geography course. To make it easy to use, each entry has a standard format. First, there is a simple definition. This is then amplified to give fuller understanding and usually includes an example. Finally, many of the entries contain an examiner's tip. These tips draw your attention to common misconceptions, ambiguities and errors of understanding.

As a tool for learning there are three possible ways of using this dictionary:

(1) To define key terms needed for A-level essay-writing and to provide succinct descriptions and explanations for short-answer questions at AS.

(2) To investigate individual topic areas such as glaciation, soils or population through extensive cross-referencing (cross-references are italicised). Try it for yourself. Select a word and draw a spider diagram to show its linkages with other words and terms. The word *glacier*, for example, connects directly to *cirques*, *ice sheets*, *icefields*, *mass balance* and *ablation*. These terms then give further linkages to *glacial*, *inter-glacial*, *quarrying*, *abrasion* and so on. In this way you can build up a clear and flexible scheme of learning which emphasises the connections within the topic.

(3) As a revision aid. Compile a checklist of essential words and terms from your AS/A-level specification document. Then search through the dictionary for the words and terms you need to know. Learn the simple definitions and examples, and make sure that you understand the terms. And, finally, don't forget the examiner's tips. Remember that success in AS and A-level geography is not just about knowledge and understanding of the subject; it is about how you *apply* your knowledge.

aa: lava with a rough, clinkery surface.

▓ Aa lava is a *basalt* lava and compared to *pahoehoe* lava is cooler and has a lower gas content.

▓ *e.g.* Many lava flows from the shield *volcanoes* of Hawaii (e.g. Mauna Loa, Kilauea) have an aa structure.

abiotic environment: non-living components of an *ecosystem*, including rocks, water, soil, gases, fire and energy.

ablation: loss of ice and snow from *glaciers* and *ice sheets* through melting, *evaporation* and sublimation (i.e. the phase change of ice to vapour).

▓ Ablation is the output from a glacier system. Together with accumulation of snow (input), ablation determines the *mass balance* of a glacier.

▓ *TIP* Remember that ablation is more than just melting.

abrasion: erosion caused by the scouring (abrading) action of rock particles transported by rivers, glaciers, waves and the wind.

▓ The importance of abrasion varies with environment and with time. In glacial environments, abrasion is a continuous process; in coastal environments, it is most important during storm conditions; and in fluvial environments, it becomes significant only at high levels of discharge. The abrasive action of sand in hot desert and semi-desert environments has little erosional effect.

▓ *e.g.* rock particles at the base of a glacier scratching, grinding and polishing rock outcrops as the glacier advances down its valley.

▓ *TIP* Remember that abrasion is often one of several erosional processes operating in a particular environment. It should not be confused with *quarrying*.

accordant coastline: type of coastline where the main rock types crop out parallel to the coast.

▓ Accordant (or Pacific) coastlines have a fairly straight planform with an absence of bays and headlands.

▓ *e.g.* the south Purbeck coastline (Dorset) where Portland Limestone runs parallel to the coast and forms a resistant barrier to erosion.

▓ *TIP* Don't confuse accordant and discordant (or Atlantic) coastlines. The latter are formed where rocks crop out at right angles to the coast, forming a series of *headlands* and *bays*.

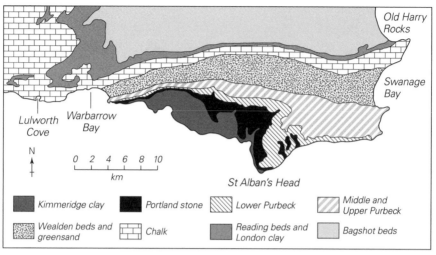

The Isle of Purbeck, Dorset: the south coast is an accordant coastline

accretion: build-up of sediments through deposition in coastal and fluvial environments.

▨ Accretion can occur only if the deposition of sediment occurs faster than erosion. The accretion of sediment is most likely to occur in low-energy environments.

▨ *e.g.* The accretion of fine sediments on *mudflats* leads eventually to their elevation a metre or two above sea level and the formation of *salt marsh*.

▨ *TIP* You should note the difference between accretion and deposition. Whereas accretion describes the accumulation of sediment, deposition simply describes a process where low energy levels cause sediment to fall out of transport.

accumulation zone: upper part of a glacier where the accumulation of snow and ice exceeds *ablation*.

acid rain: acid accumulation on vegetation and buildings caused by rainwater mixed with pollutants such as sulphur dioxide and nitrous oxides in the atmosphere.

▨ A major cause of acid rain is the release of sulphur dioxide from coal-burning power stations. Acid rain damages forests (especially coniferous trees) and plants, insects and fish in lakes and rivers. It also accelerates *chemical weathering* processes (e.g. *solution*), causing enhanced *leaching* in soils and damage to historic buildings.

▨ *e.g.* acid rain damage to forests and to aquatic life in lakes in Scandinavia caused by sulphur dioxide emissions from UK coal-burning power stations.

▨ *TIP* As a type of atmospheric pollution, you should not confuse acid rain with *global warming* and with ozone depletion (see *chlorofluorocarbons*).

acquired advantages: economic benefits of long-established urban and industrial regions.

▓ Acquired advantages include pools of skilled workers, economic and social *infrastructure*, and inter-firm linkages. These advantages were not present when a region was first industrialised.

▓ *e.g.* skilled labour and linkages between suppliers and consumers in the pottery industry in Stoke-on-Trent.

▓ *TIP* Acquired advantages most often comprise *external economies of scale* and *urbanisation economies*.

active layer: the surface metre or so of *permafrost* that melts for a few months during the summer.

▓ *TIP* Remember that processes such as *gelifluction/solifluction* and frost heave are confined to the active layer. These processes are responsible for landforms such as gelifluction sheets and lobes, earth and stone-banked terraces and some types of *patterned ground* (see *periglacial environment*).

adiabatic cooling: decrease in temperature that occurs within an air parcel which rises through the atmosphere.

▓ As an air parcel rises it expands, using up energy, which causes its internal temperature to drop. Dry air (i.e. air that has a relative *humidity* of less than 100%) cools at a rate of 10°C per km. This is known as the dry adiabatic lapse rate. Saturated air (i.e. air with 100% relative humidity and where condensation is occurring) cools at the saturated adiabatic lapse rate of 7°C per km. (See *stability* and *instability*.)

▓ *e.g.* On a warm, sunny day, a parcel of air in contact with the ground may heat up more than its surroundings. As a result, the air parcel becomes buoyant, rises as a convection current (see *convectional precipitation*) and forms *cumuliform cloud*.

▓ *TIP* Confusion about lapse rates is common. A rising parcel of air cools internally, and not by losing heat to the surrounding atmosphere. Remember that the two adiabatic lapse rates apply only to parcels of rising air. The overall decrease of temperature in the atmosphere with height is quite different. This is the *environmental lapse rate (ELR)*.

adret slope: slope facing towards the equator (see *aspect*).

▓ In middle and high latitudes, adret slopes have the most intense *insolation* and the longest hours of direct sunlight. Adret slopes have a warmer *microclimate* than poleward-facing *ubac slopes*.

▓ *e.g.* south-facing slopes in deep valleys in mountainous regions such as the Alps.

adsorption: adherence of positively charged cation nutrients (e.g. magnesium, calcium, potassium, sodium etc.) to the surface of the negatively charged clay–humus complex in the soil.

▓ Cation nutrients are removed (adsorbed) by the root hairs of plants and by *leaching*.

▓ *TIP* Take care not to confuse adsorption with absorption.

advection fog: fog that forms when relatively warm air crosses a cooler surface.

Advection fog is most common at sea and along coasts — hence its alternative name, 'sea fog'. Advection fog is most likely to develop when the temperature contrast between the air and the sea/land surface is greatest.

e.g. Advection fog is especially frequent along the northeast coast of England between the Humber and the Tweed in late spring and early summer. Known locally as 'sea fret', it forms as warm air moving westward is chilled to its *dew-point temperature* by its passage across the relatively cold North Sea.

TIP Remember that advection cooling is caused by the horizontal movement of air and that advection fog is different from *radiation fog*, which forms when the Earth's surface loses heat by radiative cooling.

afforestation: large-scale planting of an area, not previously forested, with trees.

Afforestation may take place for timber production, amenity and conservation reasons.

e.g. Kielder Forest in Northumberland is one of the largest afforestation projects in the UK.

TIP You should be able to distinguish afforestation from reafforestation. The latter describes tree planting in areas that have previously supported forests.

agglomeration economies: savings made by firms that locate in clusters and/or in large urban areas.

Clustering allows linkages between firms (e.g. between customers and suppliers), reducing transport costs and delivery times and facilitating face-to-face meetings. These advantages (which reduce unit costs) are also known as *external economies* or 'localisation economies'. Firms that locate in large urban areas also benefit from *urbanisation economies*. Large towns and cities provide an elaborate economic and social infrastructure. This infrastructure provides them with transport links, electricity, housing, schools, hospitals etc. Firms pay only a small part of the costs of these urbanisation economies.

e.g. the huge concentration of automotive parts suppliers and car assembly plants in the Tokyo region of Japan.

TIP Remember that the term 'agglomeration economies' includes both *external economies* and *urbanisation economies*.

aggradation: deposition of sediment in a river channel which causes a rise in bed elevation.

Aggradation is most likely where rivers carry large sediment loads and have high peak discharges.

e.g. braided river channels formed by meltwater streams in glaciated environments (see *braiding*).

agribusiness: large-scale, capital-intensive farming.

Agribusiness is often linked directly to other parts of the food system, such as food processing and supermarkets. Farms are often owned and controlled by large businesses that employ specialist farm managers. Agribusiness uses modern technologies such as machinery and agro-chemicals to produce cash crops for food and industry.

e.g. large-scale arable farming enterprises in East Anglia.

agro-chemicals: chemicals such as inorganic fertilisers (e.g. nitrates, phosphates), pesticides, herbicides and insecticides used in agriculture.

Agro-chemicals bring both benefits and disbenefits. They are responsible for high yields and increased food production. However, many agro-chemicals also have damaging environmental effects.

e.g. the pollution of groundwater and surface water supplies by nitrates; reductions in biodiversity caused by the application of pesticides etc. (see *nitrate pollution* and *eutrophication*).

agro-ecosystems: *ecosystems* modified by people for agricultural purposes.

Compared to natural ecosystems, agro-ecosystems have lower *biodiversity*, lower primary productivity (see *net primary production*), shorter *food chains* and less stability. Most agro-ecosystems in MEDCs depend on external inputs of *agro-chemicals*, without which they would be unsustainable (see *sustainability*).

e.g. any agricultural system, regardless of scale, technology, enterprises, etc.

airmass: very large homogeneous body of air with uniform temperature, lapse rates and humidity characteristics.

Airmasses are classified according to the region in which they form (source region) and the track they follow on leaving the source region. For air-masses affecting western Europe, the source regions are arctic, polar and tropical, and tracks are either maritime or continental. The major airmasses are arctic maritime (Am), polar maritime (Pm), polar continental (Pc), tropical maritime (Tm,) tropical continental (Tc) and returning polar maritime (rPm). Airmasses are modified on leaving their source regions. Those moving equatorwards warm and become unstable (see *instability*); those moving pole-wards cool and become stable (see *stability*). Airmasses that follow maritime tracks become more humid, while those with long continental tracks become less humid.

TIP Think of day-to-day variations in weather in the British Isles as having two causes: (a) airmass changes; and (b) the movement of weather systems such as *depressions* and *anticyclones*.

albedo: proportion of sunlight reflected from a surface.

Fresh snow and ice have the highest albedos, reflecting up to 95% of sunlight. In contrast, ocean surfaces absorb most sunlight and therefore have low albedos. Albedo can have an important influence on temperature and climate.

e.g. The Greenland ice sheet generates its own cold climate: high rates of reflection from snow and ice keep temperatures permanently low.

alluvial fan: cone of sediment deposited by a river as it leaves a gorge-like valley in a mountainous area and enters a lowland region.

As the river leaves the mountains, its energy levels suddenly fall and rapid deposition of sediment occurs.

e.g. rivers in arid and semi-arid regions (e.g. southwest USA) that drain to inland basins.

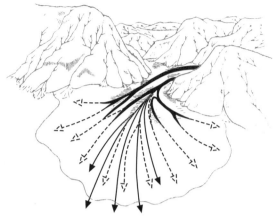

Alluvial fan development

▨ *TIP* Note the similarity between alluvial fans and *deltas*. Both form when sudden changes in a river's energy environment cause rapid deposition. The difference is that deltas form when sediments are deposited in water (e.g. sea, lakes).

alluvium: sediments deposited by streams and rivers.

▨ Alluvial sediments consist of silt, sands and gravels, and are usually stratified (i.e. sorted into layers according to size).

▨ *e.g.* *flood plains* comprising alluvium laid down within river channels and as *overbank deposits* when the river floods.

▨ *TIP* Take care not to confuse alluvium with colluvium, which describes deposits found at the base of hill slopes.

alternative farming: less intensive form of agriculture in MEDCs which relies on fewer inputs of *agro-chemicals*, is more environmentally 'friendly' and therefore is more sustainable (see *sustainability*).

▨ *TIP* *Organic farming* is a type of alternative agriculture.

alveole: small-scale weathering pit on rock surfaces.

▨ Alveoles are found on rock outcrops in hot deserts, where they are thought to result from *salt weathering*.

▨ *TIP* You should distinguish alveoles from *tafoni*. Tafoni are similar but larger-scale weathering pits in desert environments.

anabatic wind: upslope wind that develops in valleys in mountainous areas.

▨ On sunny days, air in contact with the valley sides is warmer than air at the same height over the valley. This sets up a local circulation with rising air (anabatic winds) on the valley slopes and descending air over the valley. As a result, clouds often form above the valley slopes, while skies remain clear above the valley.

▨ *TIP* Anabatic winds are often studied together with *katabatic winds*. Katabatic winds move downslope and are associated with valley fog and *temperature inversions*.

anaerobic conditions: water-saturated environment in which there is an absence of oxygen.

▓ Under anaerobic conditions, *oxidisation* does not take place and a lack of bacteria means that organic materials do not decompose.

▓ *e.g.* the formation of waterlogged horizons in gleysoils, and peat (partly decomposed plant remains) on moorlands and in lowland bogs.

▓ *TIP* Aerobic describes the opposite condition to anaerobic.

anastomosing channel: river channels that branch into sub-channels and rejoin the main channel.

▓ *e.g.* Anastomosing channels include braided channels (see *braiding*) and *distributaries* in *deltas*.

anticyclone: area of atmospheric high pressure.

▓ Anticyclones are relatively slow-moving and are associated with subsiding air throughout the *troposphere* and atmospheric *stability*. In the northern hemisphere, air circulates clockwise within anticyclones. Anticyclones bring spells of dry weather and light winds.

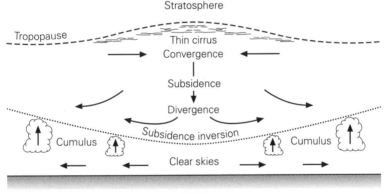

Cross-section through an anticyclone

▓ *TIP* A common misapprehension is that anticyclones produce clear skies and sunny weather. In fact, many anticyclones are cloudy. Skies may be overcast for several days — a condition known as anticyclonic gloom.

arcuate delta: river delta with a smooth, gently curving coastline.

▓ Deltas with an arcuate shape often develop where *longshore drift* leads to the formation of bars and lagoons. Eventually the shallow water lagoons disappear as they are infilled with sediment.

▓ *e.g.* the Nile delta in Egypt.

arête: knife-edged ridge between adjacent *glacial troughs* or *cirques* in glaciated uplands.

▓ Arêtes are the outcome of glacial erosion and *frost weathering* processes. Frost weathering occurred during periods when glacial uplands were not completely submerged by ice.

a

Asian 'tigers': see *newly industrialising country (NIC)*.

aspect: direction in which a slope faces.

▓ Aspect has a strong influence on local climates. It determines the intensity and amount of solar radiation received by a surface. Aspect has an important influence on the siting of settlements and agricultural land use. Slopes that face equatorwards are known as *adret slopes*. Poleward-facing slopes are *ubac slopes*.

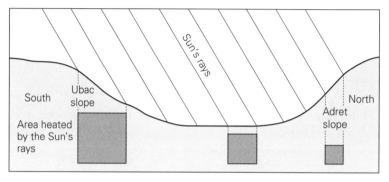

The effect of aspect on solar radiation in Britain, in June

▓ *e.g.* Viticulture in the deeply incised Mosel Valley in Germany clings to the warmer adret slopes. The colder ubac slopes are forested.

▓ *TIP* Remember that aspect determines not just the intensity of solar radiation on a surface, but also the period of direct sunlight each day. Many steep ubac slopes in high latitudes are in shadow throughout the winter.

assisted areas: areas that have acute economic, social and environmental problems and that are targeted by governments for financial help.

▓ The problems of assisted areas include high unemployment, low rates of economic growth, net migrational loss (see *net migrational change*), *social exclusion* and land dereliction. Assisted areas in the UK receive financial help from both the UK government and the EU's structural funds.

▓ *e.g.* Assisted areas in the UK include old industrial regions (e.g. South Yorkshire), remote rural regions (e.g. central Wales) and declining metropolitan regions (e.g. Merseyside).

▓ *TIP* You should be aware that the effectiveness of regional policies in assisted areas is debatable and that examination questions often focus on this issue.

atmosphere: thin envelope of gas (mainly nitrogen and oxygen) that surrounds the Earth.

▓ The atmosphere comprises four distinct layers defined by the behaviour of temperature with height. The mix of gases is very uniform with height, except that most water vapour is concentrated close to the Earth's surface. Pressure falls rapidly with height because the atmosphere is compressed into its lowest layers. Virtually all the physical processes that cause weather and climate occur in the lowest 10–15 km of the atmosphere, which is known as the *troposphere*.

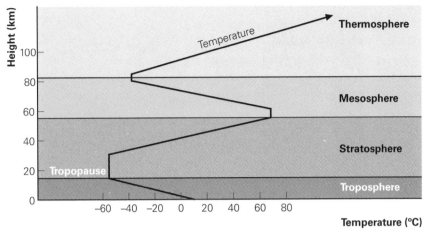

Structure of the atmosphere

▨ *TIP* The reasons why temperature falls with altitude in the troposphere are often poorly understood. The important factors are: density of the atmosphere (which affects heat transfer); concentration of heat-absorbing gases (e.g. water vapour) and particulates (e.g. dust, smoke) near the surface; and distance from the main heat source (i.e. Earth's surface).

atoll: circular coral reef, just a few metres above sea level, enclosing a lagoon.

▨ Coral atolls often form in shallow, clear water around submerged volcanic peaks. Today many atolls are threatened by rising sea level associated with global warming.

▨ *e.g.* numerous examples in Pacific island groups (e.g. Marshall Islands).

avulsion: sudden change of direction by a river into a new channel.

▨ *e.g.* the straightening of a river channel when a meander loop is cut off, leaving an abandoned channel or *oxbow lake*.

azonal soil: immature soil with poorly developed horizons and other pedogenic characteristics (see *pedogenesis*).

▨ Azonal soils are found on steep slopes, in mountainous environments, on flood plains and on newly exposed land surfaces such as lava fields and salt marshes.

▨ *e.g.* alluvial soils that receive fresh inputs of mineral material during each flood event.

▨ *TIP* Study the entries for *zonal soils* and *intrazonal soils* and clarify the difference between azonal soils and these other soil types.

backwash: water from a breaking wave that flows under gravity down a beach and returns to the sea.

■ Backwash is the opposite flow to *swash*. Its strength depends on the beach angle and the porosity of beach sediments. A powerful backwash is likely to move sand and shingle offshore, flattening beaches, and build a *breakpoint bar*.

■ *TIP* Remember that the relative strengths of backwash and swash are one of two important influences on beach profiles. The other influence is the size (and porosity) of beach sediments.

backwash effect: movement of people, capital and resources from the *periphery* to the *core* of a country or region.

■ Backwash effects are typical of the early stages of economic development. They give rise to inequalities between core and periphery and in the short term strengthen the core at the expense of the periphery. Eventually the wealth of the core diffuses to all parts of a country or region (see *cumulative causation*).

bajada: in hot arid and semi-arid regions, a series of *alluvial fans* that merge to form a continuous apron along a mountain front.

bankfull: discharge of a stream or river that just reaches the top of the banks.

■ Bankfull discharge is thought to determine the main characteristics of river channels (i.e. width, depth, hydraulic radius). It occurs infrequently (e.g. once a year or once every other year). Flows in excess of bankfull spill out of the channel and flood the surrounding valley floor.

■ *TIP* Fieldwork investigations of *hydraulic geometry* are meaningful only if variations in channel shape are related to bankfull (rather than low flow) discharge.

barchan: individual crescent-shaped *dune* with horns pointing downwind (in planform).

■ In profile, barchans have a steep slip face on their leeward side, and a longer, gentler slope exposed to the prevailing wind. They develop where sand is in short supply and the prevailing wind is from one direction.

barrier beach: long narrow beach with *swash alignment* and which forms across a bay or coastal inlet. On the landward side of the beach, there may be one or more freshwater or brackish lagoons.

▥ *e.g.* Slapton Sands in south Devon, which encloses the freshwater lagoon known as Slapton Ley.

barrier beach island: offshore beach of sand and shingle that is exposed even at high tide.

▥ Barrier beach islands often show evidence of having grown by *longshore drift* (e.g. shingle ridges or *recurved laterals*).

▥ *e.g.* Scolt Head Island in north Norfolk.

▥ *TIP* Beaches are classified according to their shape and alignment on the coast and not by their origin. Thus barrier beach islands can form by longshore drift, by sand and shingle driven onshore by wave action, or by a combination of both processes.

basal sliding: movement of warm-based glaciers by slippage on a film of water between the glacier and its bed.

▥ Up to 90% of the movement of warm-based glaciers is attributed to basal sliding.

▥ *TIP* In addition to understanding the process of basal sliding, you should be aware of the factors that influence rates of glacier movement. These factors include temperatures at the base of the glacier, slope steepness and the volume of ice in the glacier.

basalt: a basic extrusive (or volcanic) *igneous rock*.

▥ Basalt lava flows are a feature of quiet effusive eruptions. Huge outpourings of basalt lava form *lava plateaux* such as the Deccan Trappes in India. Basalt lava is usually very fluid and can flow for 20 or 30 km before solidifying. As a result it is associated with shield volcanoes (see *volcano*) such as Mauna Loa in Hawaii.

▥ *e.g.* tertiary basalt lava flows on Mull and Skye in the Inner Hebrides.

base flow: that part of stream or river flow derived from permeable rocks, soil, peat and boggy hill slopes.

▥ Base flow (also known as slow flow) is fairly constant and is mainly responsible for river flow during periods of drought and throughout the summer in the British Isles. In catchments dominated by porous rocks (e.g. chalk), most river flow comprises base flow.

▥ *TIP* Rivers with only small differences between peak flow and low flow are likely to receive most of their water from base flow.

base level: lowest level to which a river can erode its valley.

▥ Base level may be sea level, a lake or a confluence. Changes in sea level can have important effects on fluvial landforms. A fall in sea level causes renewed erosion or *rejuvenation*, leading to the formation of knickpoints, rejuvenation terraces and incised meanders. A rise in sea level results in accretion of alluvium in *estuaries* and river mouths.

batholith: major *igneous intrusion* that may be exposed at the surface by the erosion of overlying rocks.

▥ Batholiths comprise coarsely crystalline rocks, such as granite and gabbro, which cooled within the crust over thousands of years.

bay: large indentation of the coastline.

▨ Bays usually correspond with areas of less resistant rock that crop out at right angles to the coast.

▨ *e.g.* Swanage Bay, Dorset, which comprises relatively weak beds of clay.

bay-head beach: crescent-shaped beach formed at the head of a bay.

▨ Compared to an open coastline, bays have closed sediment budgets, with no input or output of sand and shingle through *longshore drift*. Wave *refraction* is complete and drift-aligned bay-head beaches form.

beach: accumulation of sand and shingle formed by wave action between the high water and low water marks.

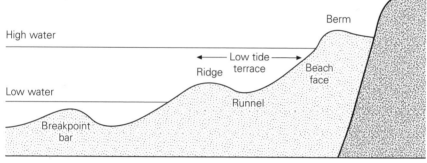

Beach profile

▨ Beaches show great variation in space and time in profile and planform. Differences in beach form reflect the influence of beach sediments, wave power and wave *refraction*.

▨ *TIP* If you are asked to explain the shape of beaches, it is important that you give consideration to both their profiles (i.e. cross-sectional shape) and their planforms.

beach nourishment: form of coastal protection where imported sand and shingle are added to a beach.

▨ Beach nourishment is designed to strengthen beaches that provide a natural protection against coastal erosion. As a type of soft engineering (see *managed retreat*), it is environmentally more acceptable than *hard engineering* alternatives such as *sea walls* and *revetments*.

bedload: coarsest fraction of a river's load, comprising pebbles, cobbles and boulders.

▨ Bedload slides and rolls along the river bed. It can be moved only at high velocities (i.e. at high discharge). The movement of bedload is the major cause of *abrasion* in river channels.

▨ *TIP* It is important to understand the relationships between bedload characteristics and (a) distance downstream (bedload gets smaller and rounder); (b) channel shape (relatively wide, shallow channels have coarser bedload than relatively deep, narrow channels).

bergschrund: deep crevasse on a *cirque* glacier that develops between the glacier and the headwall.

▨ Meltwater accumulates in the bergschrund and may assist *quarrying* on the headwall. Weathered rock particles from the cirque headwall enter the cirque glacier through the bergschrund and contribute to glacial *abrasion*.

berm: prominent ridge at the back of a beach formed by wave action.

▨ The berm represents the highest level reached by the *swash* during a tidal cycle. Berms are best developed on steeply sloping sand beaches formed by *surging breakers*.

bid rent theory: theory of competitive bidding by different land users for sites in urban areas.

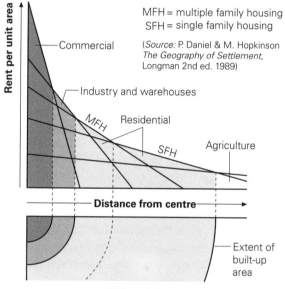

Bid rent theory

▨ The outcome of bidding is a series of *zones* (concentric rings) of land use. Bid rent theory was first developed to explain patterns of agricultural land use around market centres (see *Von Thunen*). The process of competitive bidding ensures that sites are allocated to users that can pay the highest rents/land prices. In the *central business district* (CBD), commercial activities such as retailing and office functions make the highest profits, bid the highest rents and therefore dominate land use. Every land-use type has a unique bid ren. curve that declines with distance from the CBD.

▨ *TIP* Zonal patterns of urban land use may have more than one explanation. Apart from bid rent theory, the *Burgess zonal model* based on the idea of invasion-succession (see *Burgess's zonal model*) gives a similar zonal arrangement. Remember that since the mid-twentieth century in most cities in MEDCs, planners (and not the free market) have been the major influence on urban land-use patterns.

bifurcation ratio: in the analysis of stream morphometry, the ratio of the number of streams of one order to the next highest order in a river basin.

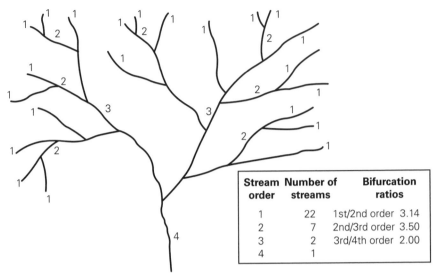

Stream order	Number of streams	Bifurcation ratios
1	22	1st/2nd order 3.14
2	7	2nd/3rd order 3.50
3	2	3rd/4th order 2.00
4	1	

Stream ordering and bifurcation ratios

■ Most bifurcation ratios vary between 2 and 4. Low values suggest well-developed stream networks, with gentle slopes, low precipitation and complete vegetation cover. Higher values are typical of steep upland catchments.

■ *e.g.* In a small river basin there are 30 second-order streams and 10 third-order streams. The bifurcation ratio is therefore 3 (i.e. 30/10).

bilateral aid: support given by one government directly to another.

■ Bilateral aid may include loans, food, manufactured goods and technical expertise.

■ *TIP* You should be clear about the distinction between bilateral and multi-lateral aid. The latter refers to aid from international organisations such as the World Bank, the International Monetary Fund and non-governmental organisations.

biodiversity: variety of species within biological communities.

■ In terrestrial *ecosystems*, biodiversity is inversely related to the number and severity of limiting factors in the physical environment. Thus cold and/or arid environments (e.g. sub-arctic, hot deserts) have low biodiversity, while warm, moist environments (e.g. tropical rainforest) have high biodiversity.

■ *TIP* You should note that the impact of human activity on ecosystems is normally to reduce biodiversity. This may be caused by deliberate action (e.g. farmers reduce biodiversity by removing species that compete with crops and domestic livestock) or by the destruction of habitats.

biogeochemical cycles: exchange of materials between living and non-living components of *ecosystems* (see *nutrient cycle*).

e.g. the cycling of carbon between rocks, the atmosphere, the oceans and living organisms.

biomass: weight of living organisms in an ecosystem expressed as either fresh weight or dry weight per hectare.

Ninety-nine per cent of biomass comprises plants. Thus the size of the biomass reflects the physical conditions for plant growth (i.e. heat and moisture).

e.g. A hectare of tropical rainforest may have a biomass of around 1,100 tonnes. In contrast, the biomass of tundra may be just 5 or 6 tonnes per hectare.

biome: *ecosystem* at a continental scale covering a large geographical area.

e.g. the *boreal forest* that covers much of northern Europe, Siberia and Canada.

biotic environment: living components of ecosystems.

The principal biotic members of ecosystems are plants, animals and decomposer organisms.

birth rate: number of births in a country (or region) during a year in proportion to the country's (or area's) population.

The birth rate (more correctly known as the 'crude birth rate' or CBR) is normally expressed as the number of live births per 1,000 of the population. The CBR varies widely between countries and between urban and rural populations.

e.g. In 1997 Niger's CBR was 54 per 1,000, compared to just 9 per 1,000 in Germany.

TIP The CBR is only an indirect measure of *fertility*. The CBR is strongly influenced by a population's age and sex structure. In a population with a large proportion of old people, the CBR will be relatively low, even though women have large families. Similar problems arise in youthful populations.

blockfield: large expanse of boulders strewn across a fairly level surface in mountainous environments.

Blockfields are the result of frost wedging in rocks that are massively jointed (i.e. the joints are widely spaced). On a level surface (e.g. a plateau), the boulders remain in situ (i.e. they are not transported by *mass movement*).

e.g. An extensive blockfield occupies the summit of the Glyders, at 900 m, in Snowdonia.

TIP Blockfields, like screes, are landforms of weathering. Unlike screes, blockfields form on level surfaces, and the rock is broken by frost action into much larger particles.

blocking: deflection of the prevailing westerly airflow to the north and south of its normal track by a large stationary *anticyclone*.

Blocking occurs in western Europe when a large anticyclone establishes itself over the continent. The blocking 'high' diverts the normal westerly flow across southern and northern Europe. Blocking may last for several days or for weeks. It causes extreme weather conditions (e.g. drought, very low winter temperatures, very high summer temperatures).

e.g. In the winter of 1962–3, a blocking high to the west of Ireland produced average temperatures of 0°C from December to February.

bluff: fairly steep-angled and prominent valley-side slope marking the boundary of a *flood plain*.

■ Bluffs are formed by lateral erosion in river channels and the migration of *meanders* across a flood plain. In planform, bluffs are usually straight. Where a river actively undercuts a bluff, it may form a steep river cliff.

boreal forest: coniferous forest that encircles the northern hemisphere in sub-polar latitudes from Alaska to Canada, Scandinavia and Siberia.

■ Conifer species include pine, fir, spruce and larch. Apart from larch, these conifers are evergreen. Their narrow, needle-shaped leaves reduce moisture loss and their evergreen habit allows them to make the most of the short growing season. Long winters and low temperatures mean that productivity is low. In the low temperatures, decomposition is slow and the high lignin content of conifer needles makes them difficult to break down. *Podzol* soils develop, the result of *leaching, cheluviation* and acidic plant litter.

bornhardt: rounded, isolated granite monolith, mainly confined to the tropics and sub-tropics.

■ Bornhardts result from sub-surface weathering of granite, concentrated along vertical joints under humid tropical conditions. The granite, rotted by *hydrolysis* (saprolite), is eventually stripped away by erosion. The isolated mass of the bornhardt survives because it is massively jointed.

■ *TIP* You should note that bornhardts, *tors* and castle kopjes are landforms that owe their development to sub-surface weathering. *Exfoliation domes*, which are similar in appearance, are probably the result of *pressure release* rather than weathering.

boss (also called 'stock'): small, usually granitic mass that was intruded and solified at depth.

■ *e.g.* Shap Fell, Cumbria.

boulder clay (also called 'till'): sediment deposited by glacial ice, which is usually poorly sorted and often contains *erratics*.

■ Boulder clay often forms glacial depositional landforms or *moraines*. However, boulder clay most often forms a thick mantle of *regolith*, which conceals the underlying bedrock and minor topographic features.

braiding: rivers that split into two or more channels, divided by bars and islands.

■ Braiding is a feature of powerful rivers, which have large and variable discharges and steep slopes. It also occurs in rivers that transport large volumes of coarse sediment. These include many meltwater rivers and rivers draining areas of loose volcanic rock.

■ *e.g.* meltwater rivers in Iceland draining from the Vatnajökull icefield and areas of loose volcanic debris.

■ *TIP* Think of braiding as a response by a river to an overload of sediment. By depositing sediment in its channel, the river steepens its gradient, thus increasing its competence and allowing transport to occur.

branch plant: factory operated by a *transnational corporation* that is involved only in routine production.

▨ Branch plants employ relatively few highly skilled workers and have neither headquarters nor research, development and design functions. They are often located in peripheral regions in MEDCs or in LEDCs, attracted by lower labour and production costs. Branch plants are relatively easy to close and are most likely to do so if a firm restructures its operations.

▨ *e.g.* Samsung's factory on Teesside making computer monitors, television tubes and fax machines.

▨ *TIP* Branch plants often increase a region's (and a country's) dependence on foreign companies. Control of much of a region's economy may be overseas and the interests of foreign firms will differ from the interests of those who live and work in regions, such as central Scotland, that have branch plant economies.

break-of-bulk: or port of railhead where there is a forced transfer of freight from one transport medium to another.

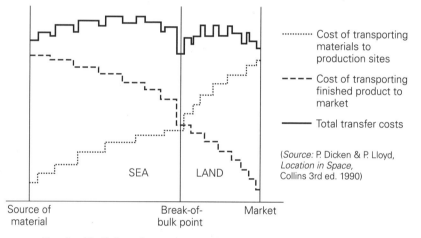

······· Cost of transporting materials to production sites

- - - - Cost of transporting finished product to market

——— Total transfer costs

(*Source:* P. Dicken & P. Lloyd, *Location in Space,* Collins 3rd ed. 1990)

SEA   LAND

Source of material   Break-of-bulk point   Market

Break-of-bulk locations as sites of minimum transport cost

▨ Break-of-bulk sites are often least-cost locations for industry. An industry locating at a break-of-bulk site where the forced transfer of freight occurs does not incur extra handling charges.

▨ *e.g.* The modern iron and steel industry in the EU and Japan locates at tidewater. This is a break-of-bulk location where imported materials such as coking coal and iron ore are shipped in.

breakpoint bar: offshore ridge of sand and shingle which runs parallel to the shore and which causes waves to break (see *beach*).

▨ Breakpoint bars are built by high-energy *surfing breakers*, which comb sand and shingle from beaches. These sediments are stored temporarily as a breakpoint bar.

brown earth: slightly acidic, base-rich *zonal soil* that forms in association with temperate deciduous forest.

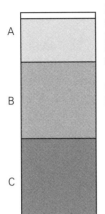

A	Litter layer. Calcareous or slightly mull litter from deciduous trees
	Dark brown silt loam or silty clay loam; fine or medium blocky peds; slightly calcareous. Calcareous or slightly acid mull litter. Some leaching
B	Brown silt loam or silty clay loam; medium or coarse blocky peds; calcareous. Some illuviation
C	Parent material (limestone)

Brown calcareous soil

▨ Brown earth soils have a fairly uniform profile and lack sharp differentiation into horizons. Mull humus that is base-rich and only mildly acidic supports large populations of soil organisms, including earthworms, which mix together the horizons. The excess of *precipitation* over *evapotranspiration* causes some *leaching*. Typical brown earths have pH values between 6.0 and 6.5.

brownfield site: site for housing, industry or commerce that has previously been developed and built on.

▨ The redevelopment of brownfield sites, many covering areas of urban dereliction, is a priority for UK planning authorities. Brownfield sites are often unattractive. They are frequently small with limited room for expansion, expensive to reclaim, difficult to access and located in run-down parts of the city. However, redevelopment of such sites is one way to encourage a renaissance in urban living in the UK, and reduce pressures on the countryside.

Burgess's zonal model: urban structure model where land use is organised as a series of concentric rings or zones around the city centre.

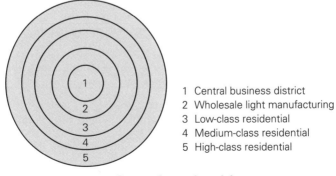

1 Central business district
2 Wholesale light manufacturing
3 Low-class residential
4 Medium-class residential
5 High-class residential

Burgess's zonal model

▨ The Burgess model was based on the urban structure of Chicago in the 1920s, i.e. a city undergoing rapid expansion and with a large influx of migrants.

Thus the model is both historically and geographically very specific and its relevance to modern cities is debatable. Burgess attributed the zonal structure of Chicago to growth caused by invasion and succession.

■ *TIP* There is no doubt that land-use zones (like sectors) exist in cities, although no city resembles Burgess's actual model. You should know that another model — *bid rent theory* — produces a similar zonal patterning, but as a result of a quite different process.

business park: purpose-built office complex that accommodates service activities, often in a landscaped setting, on the edge of town.

calcification: accumulation of calcium carbonate within a soil.

Calcification occurs in soil-forming environments where *evapotranspiration* exceeds *precipitation*. As a result, there is no excess of water to leach calcium carbonate from the soil, giving soils pH values of 7 and above.

e.g. The *chernozem* soil of mid-latitude continental grassland regions often shows calcification.

caldera: see *crater*.

calibre: size of particles transported as load by a river.

Coarse-calibre particles include cobbles and pebbles. Fine-calibre particles include sand, silt and clay.

TIP A river's ability to transport particles (its competence) depends on two factors: the size of particles and the flow velocity. You should know that the finest and coarsest particles are entrained only at very high velocities. Sand-sized particles are entrained most easily. (See *Hjulström curve*.)

canyon: steep rock-walled valley eroded by a river; often found in arid and semi-arid environments.

e.g. canyons such as the Grand Canyon on the Colorado Plateau caused by river incision and tectonic uplift.

capital-intensive industry: economic activities (e.g. agriculture, manufacturing) with heavy investment in plant, machinery, energy inputs, etc. per unit area or per employee.

Capital-intensive production is typical of economic activities that rely on higher technology levels. For this reason, capital-intensive activities are more common in MEDCs than in LEDCs.

e.g. Modern arable farming and car making are both capital-intensive economic activities.

TIP The opposite to capital intensive is labour intensive.

carbonation: solution of limestone by rain water and soil water.

Rain water and soil water contain dissolved carbon dioxide and therefore form weak carbonic acid. Carbonic acid reacts with limestone (calcium carbonate) to form calcium bicarbonate, which is soluble.

TIP Rates of carbonation depend on the acidity of rain water and soil water (i.e. the amount of carbon dioxide they contain). Soil water usually contains more carbon dioxide and is a more effective solution agent. Remember that carbonation is reversible: precipitation of calcium carbonate forms *tufa* (e.g. in *stalactites* and *stalagmites*).

carnivore: flesh-eating animal that usually occupies a position towards the end of a *food chain*.

In natural ecosystems, carnivores help to sustain the balance between herbivore populations and environmental resources. Because they occupy niches towards the end of food chains, carnivores have much smaller populations than the herbivores they predate. The predator at the end of the food chain is known as the top carnivore.

e.g. In the *boreal forest* ecosystem the wolf is the top carnivore.

carrying capacity: number of large herbivores that can graze a unit area without degrading the vegetation cover.

The limits set by carrying capacities in agro-ecosystems must be observed if farming is to be sustainable (see *sustainability*).

e.g. the payment of headage subsidies to hill farmers in the EU that has encouraged overstocking on upland pastures with resultant degrading of pastures and *soil erosion*.

TIP Carrying capacity is also used in connection with *Malthus' theory* to define the maximum sustainable population an area can support at a given standard of living.

catena: sequence of soil types found on hill slopes.

Catenas develop because soil drainage characteristics vary with position and gradient on hill slopes.

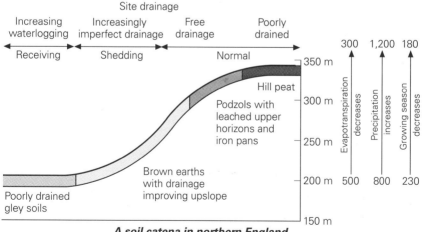

A soil catena in northern England

e.g. A typical soil catena in the Pennines might comprise: peaty gley *podzols* on flat, poorly drained summits; podzols on the free-draining slopes; and *gley soils* on poorly drained slope foot areas.

■ *TIP* Soil catenas reflect the influence of drainage. Slopes with variable geology or vegetation (i.e. most slopes) will support soils whose characteristics show the influence of other pedogenic factors (see *pedogenesis*).

cave: large void in solid rock, forming a recess or tunnel, and developed along lines of structural weakness such as joints, bedding planes and faults.

■ Caves are common along cliffed coastlines and in areas of hard limestone. In coastal environments, caves result from marine erosion. In limestone areas, caves form by solution along joints and bedding planes.

■ *e.g.* Meregill Hole in the Yorkshire Dales, formed by solution of Carboniferous limestone; Fingal's Cave, a sea cave on Staffa (western Scotland), formed by marine erosion of columnar basalt.

■ *TIP* In limestone areas, you should distinguish *vadose caves*, irregular in cross-section and formed by solution of underground streams; and *phreatic caves*, formed below the water table and tube-like in cross section.

cavernous weathering: weathering processes that result in rock surfaces pitted with small holes and depressions.

■ Cavernous weathering is common in deserts and coastal environments. This suggests that salt is probably a key process in cavernous weathering. The term 'honeycomb weathering' describes high concentrations of small weathering pits.

■ *e.g.* Large weathering pits in hot arid and semi-arid environments known as *alveoles* and *tafoni* are associated with cavernous weathering.

CBD: see *central business district*.

central business district (CBD): central area of a town or city dominated by commercial land uses, especially offices and retailing.

■ The CBD has several other distinguishing characteristics: high-intensity land use, high-rise buildings, high rents and land values, high pedestrian and traffic flows and high accessibility levels.

■ *TIP* You should recognise that the principal advantages of the CBD for commercial activities — access to customers and economies of clustering — have been steadily eroded in the last 30 years. High rents, shortages of space and chronic congestion have encouraged many commercial activities to decentralise and relocate in the suburbs.

centrality: importance or status of a central place.

■ We can measure centrality in several ways: population size, total number of functions, number of different functions, retail floorspace, size of built area, employment, size of trade area, *connectivity* to the road or rail network etc.

■ *e.g.* In Norfolk, Norwich has higher centrality than any other settlement.

■ *TIP* You should know that centrality has nothing to do with geographical position or situation.

centrally planned economy: see *command economy*.

central place theory: theory first proposed by the German geographer Walter Christaller to explain the distribution and hierarchy of service centres or central places.

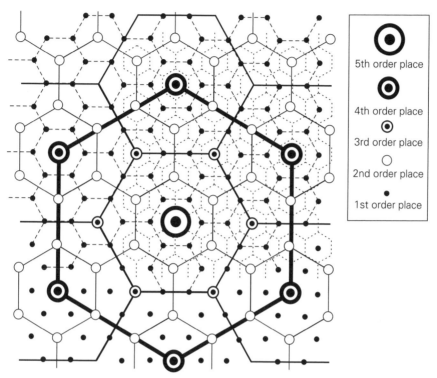

⊙	5th order place
⊙	4th order place
⊙	3rd order place
○	2nd order place
•	1st order place

Idealised pattern of settlement according to central place theory

▨ Central place theory shows how, under idealised conditions, central places should be distributed (i.e. uniformly, with each central place serving a hexagonal market area and the central places forming a triangular lattice). The size of market areas is proportional to the status of the central place. In Christaller's $K = 3$ system (based on the market principle), each central place serves its own population and the populations of two other lower-order centres. The result is a hierarchy that progresses by a factor of 3.

▨ *e.g.* In the UK there is some correspondence between central place theory and long-established settlement patterns in lowland agricultural regions such as the Vale of York and East Anglia. Elsewhere new settlement patterns and the location of service centres have been planned using the principles of central place theory, e.g. the Zuider Zee polders in the Netherlands and the Negev Desert in Israel.

▨ *TIP* Central place theory does not set out to explain actual settlement patterns. Instead it isolates a single variable (e.g. access to market), holds all other variables constant and describes an idealised outcome. It gives us an insight into how one factor influences the spacing and hierarchy of settlement.

centre of gravity: mean centre of a point distribution on a map.

▨ To find the centre of gravity of a point distribution, we calculate the mean values for the coordinates (eastings and northings) for the points.

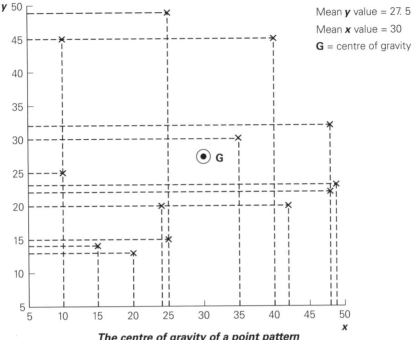

The centre of gravity of a point pattern

CFCs: see *chlorofluorocarbons*.

channel capacity: maximum discharge that a stream channel can accommodate before excess water spills onto the *flood plain*.

chelation: type of chemical weathering where plant debris and rainwater form weak organic acids, which cause rock minerals to break down.

▩ Chelation is most effective in humid tropical environments that have abundant moisture and support a dense vegetation cover.

cheluviation: downwashing of solid particles of mineral and organic matter from the upper horizons of *podzol* soils by rainwater and weak humic acids.

▩ *e.g.* Cheluviation is an important process in the development of podzolic soils. It is often associated with vegetation that produces acidic leaf litter (e.g. coniferous forest, heather and ling).

▩ *TIP* It is worth remembering that cheluviation is a combination of two processes: *chelation* and *eluviation*.

chemical weathering: in situ breakdown of rocks exposed at or near the Earth's surface by chemical processes.

▩ The rates and types of chemical weathering vary with climate. Ideal conditions are warm and wet. Chemical weathering is least effective in arid and cold climates.

▩ *e.g.* The main chemical weathering processes are *solution, hydrolysis, hydration* and *oxidation*.

chernozem: type of *zonal soil* found in cool, temperate continental grasslands.

C

■ Chernozems have an unusually high organic content, which is responsible for their black coloration. They are well drained, neutral to slightly alkaline and, because of their fertility, intensively cultivated.

■ *e.g.* the soils of the drier western Prairies of Canada and the USA.

chestnut soil: type of zonal soil found in the wetter regions of cool temperate grasslands.

■ Chestnut soils form in climatic environments where a small excess of *precipitation* over *evaporation* causes some *leaching*. As a result, these soils are slightly acidic. Like *chernozems*, chestnut soils are intensively cultivated.

■ *e.g.* the soils of the wetter eastern Prairies of Canada and the USA.

chi-squared test: inferential statistical test which compares the differences between an observed distribution and a theoretical one that would develop under random conditions.

■ Chi-squared is used to examine the differences between sample distributions. Unlike many statistical tests, the population from which the samples are drawn does not have to follow a normal frequency distribution.

■ *e.g.* comparing the frequency of occurrence of marram grass in a sand dune ecosystem with distance inland from the seashore.

■ *TIP* Chi-squared can only be used with frequency distribution data that comprise absolute values (not percentages). The data should be presented as a contingency table and only a small proportion of cells should contain expected values of less than 5.

chlorofluorocarbons (CFCs): synthetic gases used as propellants in aerosols, refrigerants and plastic foam packaging.

■ Complex chemical reactions between chlorine from CFCs, sunlight and ice particles are responsible for the destruction of ozone in the stratosphere. The thinning of the ozone layer increases the amount of ultraviolet radiation reaching the Earth's surface. This in turn threatens human health (increasing the risks of skin cancer and eye cataracts), damages crops and destroys plankton, which is at the base of the oceans' *food chain*.

■ *TIP* Many students confuse ozone depletion with *global warming*. Although CFCs are greenhouse gases, ozone depletion is not affected by rising levels of carbon dioxide or methane in the atmosphere.

choropleth map: proportional shading map based on areal units such as local authority areas or postcode areas.

■ *e.g.* a county map showing levels of unemployment in journey-to-work areas.

■ *TIP* A successful choropleth map will convey a clear image of spatial patterns. The choice of number of classes and class intervals is crucial. A balance is needed between excessive generalisation and excessive detail. The size of areal units affects the accuracy of the map. Large units may have considerable internal variability, which will not appear on a choropleth map. Because they are based on areas, choropleth maps often give a misleading impression of abrupt change at area boundaries.

cirque (also called 'corrie', 'coire' and 'cwm'): bowl-shaped hollow, surrounded by steep slopes on three sides, located in a former glaciated upland.

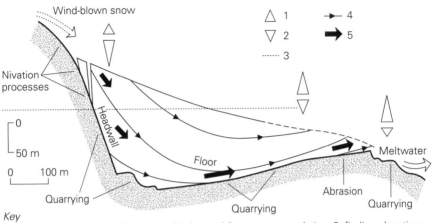

Key
Relative annual amounts of 1, gross ablation and 2, gross accumulation; 3, firnline elevation; 4, internal flow lines; 5, relative flow velocity (proportional to line)

Cirque glacier mass balance, flow and process

■ During the last *glacial*, cirque hollows were occupied by small *glaciers*. Processes such as *abrasion*, *quarrying* and the rotational movement of ice excavated the hollow. The steep headwall exposed above the glacier was also cut back by *frost weathering*.

■ *e.g.* Blea Water below High Street in the Lake District.

■ *TIP* Cirques can only form during periods of limited ice cover, when glaciers are confined to valleys. Remember that during the glacial maximums, the entire landscape was submerged beneath ice a kilometre or more in thickness.

cirrus cloud: high-altitude cloud made up of ice crystals and with a fibrous, feathery appearance.

■ Cirrus clouds are too thin to produce *precipitation*. However, they often form on the leading edge of a *warm front*, and precede the arrival of thick cloud and prolonged precipitation.

climax vegetation: type of vegetation that is the final stage of *plant succession*.

■ Climax vegetation is in equilibrium with the local/regional climate and other environmental influences. Provided the environment remains constant, climax vegetation will persist unchanged. Compared to earlier successional stages, climax vegetation often has greater *biodiversity*, *biomass*, energy and nutrient flows, productivity and stability.

■ *e.g.* At a global scale, climax vegetation types are known as *biomes* (e.g. the tropical rainforest and *tundra*).

■ *TIP* Climax vegetation is usually most strongly influenced by climate. However, you should be aware that climax vegetation can also result from a combination of climate and other environmental factors (*sub-climax*), and human activities (*plagioclimax*).

cockpit karst: see *karst*.

coire: alternative name for a *cirque*.

cold front: trailing edge of the warm sector in a *depression* where tropical air is replaced by polar air (see *warm front*).

■ Warm air rises steeply at the cold front, undercut by cold air and sucked upwards by the cold front jet. Extensive cloud (including cumulo-nimbus) forms at the cold front and *precipitation* is heavy and sometimes thundery.

■ *TIP* You should know and understand the sequence of weather changes that occur at the approach, during the passage and in the rear of the cold front.

collective agriculture: form of socialist agriculture in which farmers join together to provide labour for their common benefit and to meet production targets set by the state.

■ Collectives give farmers more say in their farms' success than state farms. Although the land remains state-owned, it is leased permanently to farm workers, who run the collective as a single unit, with labour organised into teams. The workers share their profits.

■ *e.g.* North Korea, where virtually all agricultural production comes from collectives and state farms.

■ *TIP* Collective agriculture and cooperative agriculture are essentially the same system.

command economy (also called 'centrally planned economy'): economy in which production is directed by the government through the ownership and control of farms, factories and shops.

■ *e.g.* North Korea.

■ *TIP* With the demise of world communism, few command economies survive today. Most communist countries have accepted some economic liberalisation in the last 15 years or so. China is the outstanding example of this changing attitude.

comparative advantage: economic benefit that arises when a country or region specialises in the production of goods for which it has a particular advantage (e.g. materials, low labour costs, skills).

■ A country may have an absolute advantage in the production of two goods, A and B (i.e. it can make them at lowest unit cost). However, by specialising in the production of A it can make the higher profits. This allows another region to specialise in the production of B, in which it will have a comparative (but not an absolute) advantage.

■ *e.g.* nineteenth-century regional industrial specialisation, such as the manufacture of iron and steel in south Wales and cotton textiles in Lancashire.

■ *TIP* Note that free trade and the removal of import barriers favour comparative advantage (i.e. they encourage countries to specialise in goods they can produce most cost-effectively).

comparison goods: durables such as clothes and furniture that are purchased only after comparison of prices and quality.

■ Comparison goods are relatively expensive and purchased infrequently. This means that they have high *thresholds* and tend to be concentrated in higher-order service centres.

competence: ability of a stream or river to transport load of a given size or *calibre*.

compressive flow: type of internal flow in *glaciers* characterised by an upward component of ice movement along slip lines.

■ Compressive flow occurs below the firnline (see diagram on page 26) and in areas where there is a reduction in flow velocity and/or gradient.

■ *e.g.* the internal flow of ice in a cirque from the floor zone to the threshold or lip.

condensation: phase change of water from vapour to liquid.

■ Condensation occurs when water vapour is chilled to its *dew-point temperature* and the air becomes saturated. Water vapour is normally cooled by: (a) contact with the Earth's surface; (b) rising through the atmosphere and expanding (*adiabatic cooling*). The main atmospheric effects of condensation are clouds, *fog* and *dew*.

connectivity: extent to which places in a transport network are connected directly to each other.

■ The connectivity of a transport network can be described if the network is reduced to a series of nodal points (vertices) and routes (edges). The simplest connectivity measurement is the ratio of edges to vertices. This is the beta index.

■ *e.g.* The beta index for network A is 1.5, which has better connectivity than network B (beta index of 1.0).

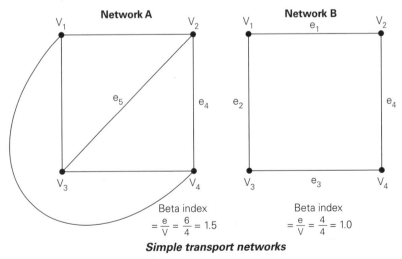

Simple transport networks

■ *TIP* Because network analysis reduces transport networks to a graph of straight lines and points, physical distances have no significance. An alternative name for this type of graph is a *topological map*.

conservative plate boundary: tectonic plate boundary where two plates shear past each other and where crust is neither formed nor destroyed.

■ *e.g.* the San Andreas fault in southern and central California, which is the boundary between the Pacific and North American plates.

constructive plate boundary: tectonic plate boundary where new oceanic crust forms (see *mid-ocean ridges*).

■ *e.g.* the mid-Atlantic ridge which in the northern hemisphere is the boundary between the Eurasian and North American plates.

continental drift: theory that the continents are mobile and over geological time have shifted their position on the Earth's surface.

■ The idea of continental drift goes back to the seventeenth century when the first accurate maps of the Atlantic Ocean showed a remarkable 'fit' between the coastlines of Africa and South America. Geological and fossil evidence added further support to the idea that the continents once formed a single super-continent — Pangaea. The process responsible for continental drift (only discovered in the 1960s) is *seafloor spreading*.

■ *e.g.* the opening of the Atlantic Ocean 70 million years ago as North America and Eurasia drifted apart. The Atlantic Ocean continues to widen today at a rate of 2.5 cm a year.

continentality: dominating influence of very large land masses on climate.

■ Locations in the centre of large land masses are dominated by the thermal properties of land. Distant oceans, which moderate climatic extremes, have little influence here. Land heats up rapidly in summer, but loses its heat quickly in winter. Thus summer temperatures are above the average for the latitude and winter temperatures are well below the average. This gives a very large mean annual range of temperature — the main feature of continental climates. Distance from the oceans accounts for the relatively low *precipitation*, most of which falls in summer convectional showers.

■ *e.g.* Winnipeg (latitude 50°N) in Manitoba has a mean July temperature of +19.5°C and a mean January temperature of –19.5°C.

■ *TIP* The opposite of continentality is *oceanicity*. Oceanicity dominates the British Isles' climate, and is just as anomalous (and therefore extreme) as continentality.

contour ploughing: ploughing land across a slope rather than up and down it.

■ Contour ploughing is a soil conservation technique that helps to reduce erosion by *runoff*. Ploughing across the slope means that the ridges and furrows act as barriers to the downslope movement of water and soil.

convectional precipitation: high-intensity, short-duration precipitation events from *cumuliform clouds*.

■ Convectional precipitation occurs in unstable atmospheric conditions (see *instability*) associated with rising parcels of relatively warm air. The rising air (convection currents or thermals) cools, condenses and forms thick cumuliform clouds. Hail and thunder often accompany convectional downpours. The most common causes of convection are: sun heating the surface, making the overlying air warmer and less dense than its surroundings; and cool air moving across a relatively warm surface (e.g. at a *cold front*).

▓ *TIP* Heavy convectional precipitation and thunderstorms indicate a great depth of *instability* in the lower atmosphere and cumuliform clouds several kilometres high.

convenience goods and services: low-cost goods and services that are purchased frequently.

▓ Convenience goods and services have low *thresholds* and are therefore the only form of retailing in the low-order central places.

▓ *e.g.* food shops, hairdressers.

cooperative agriculture: see *collective agriculture*.

coral reef: low ridge of coral found in clear, shallow, tropical seas.

▓ Coral is formed by polyps, which build cup-like shells around themselves by secreting calcium carbonate. The hard shells accumulate to form coral reefs and islands.

▓ *e.g.* the Great Barrier Reef, Queensland, Australia.

▓ *TIP* Coral reefs are the most spectacular example of the construction of a coastal landform by organic activity.

core: see *Friedmann's core–periphery model*.

core and frame model: model of the spatial structure of the central business district (CBD) which recognises an inner zone of higher-intensity land use and an outer zone of lower-intensity use.

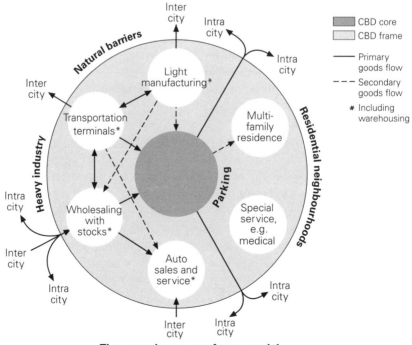

The central area core-frame model

◼ The inner zone of the CBD has tall multistorey buildings, high rentals and heavy pedestrian traffic, and is dominated by *multiple retailers* and office-based services. The outer zone has lower-rise buildings, lower rentals, more independent retailers and shops that belong to small multiple chains. Wholesaling and warehousing are important in the frame as well as retailing, which requires extensive sites (e.g. car showrooms).

◼ *TIP* The CBD is not an area of uniform land use. You should recognise that spatial contrasts in land use in the CBD reflect differences in accessibility and rent levels.

Coriolis force: deflection of a moving body on the Earth's surface arising from the Earth's rotation.

◼ The Coriolis force deflects the wind to the right in the northern hemisphere and to the left in the southern hemisphere.

◼ *e.g.* the northeast trade winds, which in the absence of the Coriolis force would blow directly from the sub-tropical 'high' to the equatorial 'low' (i.e. from north to south).

◼ *TIP* The Coriolis force is an 'apparent' force. This means that the deflection is only apparent to an observer standing on the (rotating) Earth. To an observer in space, the trade winds would follow a simple north–south trajectory.

correlation: statistical test that measures the association between two or more variables.

◼ Simple correlation involves two variables: x, the independent or causal variable, and y, the dependent variable. The assumption is that changes in x influence changes in y. The strength of the relationship between x and y is measured by a correlation coefficient that ranges in value from +1 to −1. +1 is a perfect positive correlation; −1 is a perfect negative or inverse correlation; and 0 is no correlation at all. The two most widely used correlation tests are the Spearman rank correlation (r_s) and the product moment correlation (r).

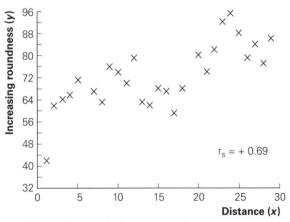

(a) The relationship between sediment roundness and distance downstream: Marshaw Wyre, Lancashire

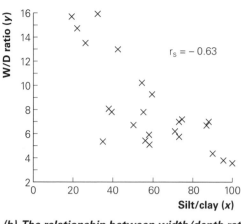

(b) The relationship between width/depth ratio and bank material: Marshaw Wyre, Lancashire

▨ *e.g.* the inverse correlation between urban land values (*y*) and distance from the city centre (*x*).

▨ *TIP* If you have a data set of arranged pairs which can be plotted as a scatter-graph, it should be possible to use a correlation test. However, before using the test be sure to identify independent and dependent variables.

corrie: alternative name for a *cirque*.

counterurbanisation: decentralising movement of population in MEDCs away from cities and conurbations, to small towns and villages in commuter hinterlands, and to remoter rural areas.

▨ In the UK counterurbanisation began in the 1960s, but had weakened by the 1990s. Among its causes are increased personal mobility provided by car ownership, dissatisfaction with the quality of life in large urban areas (e.g. congestion, crime, services, pollution), decentralisation of many jobs, retirement migration and self-employed people working from home.

▨ *e.g.* the massive decline of most metropolitan districts in the UK since 1961 (e.g. Merseyside), and the complementary population growth in adjacent rural counties (e.g. Cheshire).

crater: circular depression in the ground caused by surface subsidence after a volcanic eruption and the emptying of a *magma chamber*.

▨ A *caldera* is a volcanic crater formed by subsidence, only on a much larger scale.

▨ *e.g.* the Halemaumau crater that occupies a small part of the much larger Kilaeau summit caldera on Hawaii's Big Island.

craton (also called 'shield area'): large, tectonically stable area of low relief formed from ancient crystalline rocks.

▨ *e.g.* the Baltic Shield in Finland and Sweden composed of gneiss, granite and other crystalline rocks.

crop rotation: method of farming that avoids growing the same crop in a field continuously.

Crop rotations maintain soil fertility and reduce the risks from pests and diseases.

e.g. A typical crop rotation in eastern England might comprise one year each of wheat and oil seed rape, followed by a two-year ley of sown grass.

crude birth rate: see *birth rate*.

crude death rate: see *death rate*.

cuesta: see *escarpment*.

cumulative causation: theory proposed by Gunnar Myrdal that *initial advantages* to industrial and economic growth in a region lead to a series of virtuous growth cycles.

Cumulative causation is an example of positive feedback in an economic system. Initial economic growth creates employment, a demand for labour and the expansion of local markets. The emergence of skilled labour, markets and *external economies* triggers further investment, leading to another cycle of growth. In its early stages, growth takes place in the *core* at the expense of the *periphery*. These so-called *backwash effects* generate marked regional differences in prosperity. Eventually, diseconomies in the core (see *urbanisation diseconomies*), such as high labour costs, congestion and high rents, force economic activities to disperse to the periphery. Regional disparities in wealth narrow as these so-called 'spread' effects take hold.

cumuliform cloud: cloud with a flat base, rounded top and generally lumpy appearance.

Cumuliform clouds develop in unstable (see *instability*) atmospheric conditions and are the visible evidence of rising currents of warm air. There are several types of cumuliform cloud. Fair weather cumulus clouds have no great vertical development and are not associated with precipitation. In contrast, cumulonimbus clouds may fill the whole of the *troposphere*. They produce thunderstorms, hail, high-intensity precipitation and violent downdraughts of cold air.

cwm: alternative name for *cirque*.

death rate: number of deaths in an area per 1,000 of the population.

▓ Several factors influence death rates, including the age structure of a population, the quality of health care, environmental conditions and diet.

▓ *TIP* A common mistake is to assume that the death rate and *mortality* are the same. Because the death rate is strongly affected by age structure, it does not measure mortality accurately. In 1997 the death rate for the UK's relatively aged population was 11 per 1,000, compared with 9 per 1,000 for India's more youthful population. However, life expectancy for females in the UK was 79 years in 1997, compared with 61 years for females in India.

deforestation: destruction of forests by deliberate felling, firing or the grazing and browsing of domestic animals (preventing regeneration).

▓ Deforestation destroys habitats, reduces *biodiversity* and results in increased surface *runoff* and *soil erosion*. It contributes significantly to *land degradation*.

▓ *e.g.* Large-scale deforestation (the result of logging, agriculture and mining) is currently taking place in tropical rainforests in countries such as Indonesia and Brazil.

deglaciation: retreat of ice from an area following a glacial episode.

▓ Deglaciation follows a climatic warming, which causes a negative *mass balance* in *glacier* (or *ice sheet*) budgets. The impact of deglaciation on landforms is considerable. Retreating ice fronts leave behind lateral, terminal and hummocky *moraines*. Powerful meltwater streams produce *eskers, kames* and *sandar* (outwash plains).

▓ *e.g.* the glacial valleys (e.g. Thorsmark) and coastal plains (sandar) of southern Iceland.

▓ *TIP* Deglaciation and its associated landforms did not just occur with the ending of the last Devensian glacial. Today in most glaciated areas, glaciers are retreating and deglaciation is taking place.

deindustrialisation: sudden and steep decline of a country's or region's industrial base.

▓ Deindustrialisation hit many specialised industrial regions in MEDCs in the 1970s and 1980s. Worst affected were regions overdependent on low-technology industries such as textiles, or heavy industries such as steel and shipbuilding. The main outcome of deindustrialisation was high levels of un-employment.

■ *e.g.* northeast England, where deindustrialisation between 1975 and 1990 led to the massive contraction of coal mining, steel making and shipbuilding.

■ *TIP* You should think of deindustrialisation as part of (a) the structural shift of employment in MEDCs from industry to service activities; (b) the *globalisation* of the world economy.

delta: extensive triangular-shaped area of fine sediment at a river's mouth extending beyond the trend of the adjacent coastline.

■ Deltas form when the rate of sedimentation exceeds the rate of sediment removal by wave and tidal action. Rivers transporting very large suspended sediment loads or discharging into tideless seas are most likely to form deltas. Deposition of fluvial sediment within channels in deltas produces multiple-thread channels or *distributaries*.

■ *e.g.* The Nile Delta has a smooth arcuate planform, caused by active wave transport processes. The Mississippi Delta has a bird's foot planform. Low-energy wave and tidal action allows distributaries and their levees to advance seaward to give this unique bird's foot planform.

demographic transition: changes in *fertility* and *mortality* (i.e. vital rates) that accompany economic development.

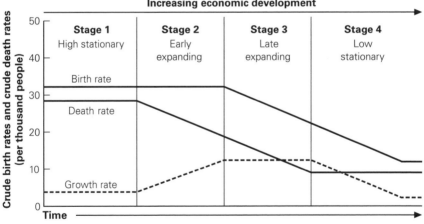

The demographic transition

■ In pre-industrial economies, both fertility and mortality rates are high, resulting in little natural increase. In *post-industrial economies*, both fertility and mortality fall to low levels, and again produce minimal natural increase. However, this transition is neither immediate nor smooth. In the demographic transition's second stage, fertility remains high while mortality drops steeply. This gives rapid population growth. Although fertility begins to fall in stage 3, rapid growth continues because mortality remains at a lower level. Thus the progress from pre-industrial to post-industrial economies leads to an imbalance in fertility and mortality, and to explosive population growth.

■ *e.g.* the growth of population in the UK between 1800 and 1950.

■ *TIP* There is no certainty that LEDCs will undergo a demographic transition. The transition model is based on the experiences of countries in western Europe. Social, economic, technological and demographic conditions are very different in many LEDCs and the demographic outcome of economic change could be quite different.

dendritic drainage: network of stream and river channels similar to the branching pattern of a tree.

■ Dendritic drainage networks represent random patterns and are often found in areas of uniform geology and structure.

dependency: subordinate position of LEDCs in relation to MEDCs within the global economy.

■ LEDCs depend on MEDCs for imports of industrial goods, markets for their primary exports, *foreign direct investment*, loans, technology, aid, etc. The terms of trade often work against LEDCs, leaving many in permanent debt to MEDCs.

dependency ratio: ratio of the total number of children (15 and under) and old people (60 or 65 and over) to economically active adults in a population.

■ Dependency ratios may be high in populations with (a) a large proportion of children; (b) a large proportion of old people. A high level of dependency in a population has important implications for health care, education, pensions, etc.

■ *e.g.* Zambia has a youthful population and therefore a high dependency ratio. Forty-nine per cent of its population are aged 15 and under, and 4 per cent are over 60. Thus its dependency ratio is 53/47 or 1.13. This means that for every adult there are 1.13 dependants.

■ *TIP* Remember that high dependency ratios are a feature of both LEDCs and MEDCs, but for different reasons. In LEDCs, most dependants are children; in MEDCs, old people add significantly to the burden of dependency.

depression: large, travelling low-pressure area that dominates the weather in middle and high latitudes.

■ In northwestern Europe, most depressions follow a west to east track and bring unsettled, wet and windy conditions. Depressions are a response to the *global energy budget*. They transport the energy surplus from the tropics to polar regions. Most of the weather (cloud and *precipitation*) in depressions is found along *fronts* where air rises to the level of the *tropopause*. On satellite images, these frontal systems show up as organised bands of thick cloud.

■ *TIP* You should learn the sequence of weather changes that occur as a depression, with its associated fronts, moves across a region. Try to relate these weather changes to the airmasses that form depressions and to the processes operating at the fronts.

desert: harsh environment that, owing to extreme drought or extreme cold or both, supports little or no plant and animal life.

d

▨ Deserts are defined biologically. Few deserts support no life at all. The severe conditions for life in deserts mean that productivity, *biomass* and *biodiversity* are low.

▨ *e.g.* The Sahara is the world's largest hot arid desert; Antarctica is the world's largest cold desert.

▨ *TIP* Tropical arid deserts are not just defined by their low annual rainfall. It is the balance of rainfall and *evapotranspiration* that determines how much moisture is available to support plants.

desertification: reduction in agricultural capacity in an area as a result of human and/or natural processes.

▨ Desertification is associated with a reduction in productivity (crops, livestock, firewood, etc.) and an absolute decline in soil, water, timber and grazing resources. Most often desertification is the outcome of human mismanagement and natural processes such as climatic change.

▨ *TIP* It is a misconception to imagine that desertification leads to the development of full desert conditions. It is rarely a dramatic process; rather it contributes to *land degradation*, which affects around one-quarter of the world's drylands.

desert varnish: thin patina of iron and manganese oxide that covers many rock surfaces in hot deserts.

destructive plate boundary: see *subduction zone*.

development stage model: see *Rostow model*.

dew: condensation that leaves a deposit of water on vegetation and other surfaces at or near the ground.

▨ Dew forms when radiative cooling (usually at night) causes the air near the ground to reach its saturation point. Conditions favouring dew formation include clear skies, a light breeze and humid air.

dew-point temperature: temperature at which air becomes saturated with vapour and *condensation* occurs.

▨ *TIP* Remember that the dew-point temperature depends on the humidity of the air. An air parcel at 15°C with 95% humidity will require only slight cooling to reach its dew-point. In contrast, an air parcel at the same temperature but with only 50% humidity will experience a much greater drop in temperature to become saturated.

diffluent col: trough eroded by a lateral branch of a *glacier* that has spilled over a pre-glacial divide.

diffusion: process by which a new idea or a new product spreads over geographical space from a place of origin.

▨ Several factors influence the rate and direction of spatial diffusion (e.g. population density and distribution, transport and communications technology, physical barriers to movement). Classic diffusion models assume that diffusion occurs primarily through word of mouth. This results in a 'neighbourhood effect' (i.e. the probability of diffusion is inversely related to the distance separating a teller and a potential receiver). The probability of a receiver adopting an innovation also depends on personal characteristics such as age, education and socio-economic status.

▧ *e.g.* the diffusion of *high-yielding varieties* of rice in south Asia as part of the *green revolution*.

dilatation: see *pressure release*.

dip slope: longer, gentler slope of an *escarpment* (or cuesta).

▧ Escarpments form by the regional folding of strata. The gradient of the dip slope reflects the structure (i.e. angle of folding) of the strata.

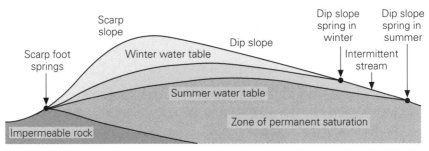

Dip and scarp slopes and springs on an escarpment

▧ *e.g.* the gentle southern slope of the chalk South Downs which descends from the scarp crest down to the coast of the English Channel.

diseconomies of scale: see *urbanisation diseconomies*.

dispersed settlement: pattern of settlement dominated by isolated farms.

▧ Dispersed settlement in western Europe is typical of upland regions, where limited resources (e.g. infertile soils, steep slopes, poor drainage) give rise to extensive farming. In these circumstances, only farms with large hectarages are viable. Logistically, it is impossible for such farms to cluster to form villages.

▧ *e.g.* the pattern of rural settlement in Upper Teesdale in the northern Pennines.

▧ *TIP* It would be wrong to think that physical factors alone cause dispersed settlement patterns. Human factors such as the absence of a feudal system in much of Britain north of the Tees–Exe line in the Middle Ages, and the enclosure movement in eighteenth-century England, also created dispersed settlement patterns.

distributary: river channel that branches from the main channel in a *delta*.

▧ Unlike *braided* channels, distributaries do not rejoin the main channel. The diversion of flow into branching channels is the result of fluvial deposition within the main channel.

▧ *e.g.* The River Rhône, on entering its delta just south of Arles, branches into two major distributaries: the Grand Rhône and the Petit Rhône.

▧ *TIP* Distributaries are the opposite of tributaries, which are smaller streams or rivers that join a larger stream or river.

doline: surface depression in an area of Carboniferous limestone.

▧ Dolines are a classic landform of *karst* scenery. They are the result of sub-surface solution of limestone. Some dolines (e.g. those with very steep sides) are caused by the collapse of caves and caverns. Others are formed by subsidence (e.g. *shake holes*).

▓ *e.g.* Hull Pot (a collapse doline) on the western flanks of Penyghent in Upper Ribblesdale.

dormitory settlement: see *exurbs*.

drainage basin: area drained by a river and its tributaries.

drumlin: low, rounded hill made of glacial till and formed by deposition beneath an *ice sheet*.

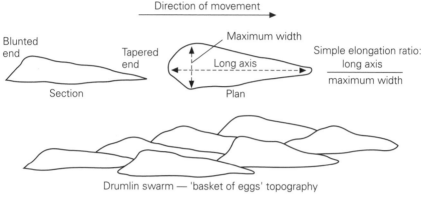

Direction of movement

Blunted end

Tapered end

Maximum width

Long axis

Simple elongation ratio:
$$\frac{\text{long axis}}{\text{maximum width}}$$

Section

Plan

Drumlin swarm — 'basket of eggs' topography

Drumlin: planform and profiles

▓ Drumlins usually occur in swarms, with their long axes parallel to the direction of ice movement and with the blunt, steeper end pointing up-glacier. There is no definitive explanation of how drumlins form, though their streamlined form suggests moulding by moving ice.

▓ *e.g.* the Craven Lowlands, between Skipton and Settle in north Yorkshire.

dry farming: system of cultivation that relies for moisture on direct rainfall.

▓ In semi-arid regions, farmers may conserve soil moisture by shallow ploughing, zero tillage (i.e. planting seeds in fields of unploughed stubble), dressing the soil with mulch to reduce *evaporation*, leaving fields fallow, etc. Dry farming is especially vulnerable in years of below average rainfall and drought.

▓ *e.g.* large-scale commercial grain cultivation in the prairies of Canada and the US Midwest.

▓ *TIP* You should know that the security of cultivation in dryland regions can be greatly improved by supplementing direct rainfall with irrigation water.

dry valley: river-eroded valley that no longer has a permanent stream or river.

▓ In the British Isles, dry valleys are most common in areas of *permeable rocks* such as chalk, Carboniferous limestone and Jurassic limestone. Dry valleys may have formed: (a) when the *water table* was much higher than today and surface *runoff* occurred; (b) during *periglacial* conditions when *permafrost* created an impermeable surface and meltwater eroded the surface.

▓ *e.g.* the dry valleys cut in the dip slope of the chalk South Downs.

TIP The puzzle of dry valleys is that they were eroded by streams and rivers that no longer flow on the surface. The key to understanding this is to explain how areas of permeable rock might once have supported surface runoff.

dune: accumulation of sand forming a low hill or ridge in hot arid and coastal environments.

Dunes form as a result of sand deposition. In hot arid environments, deposition occurs on sandy rather than rocky surfaces. Dunes in deserts show a variety of forms depending on the direction of the dominant wind. Small crescent-shaped dunes with a steep slip-face oriented downwind are aligned at right angles to the dominant wind (see *barchan*). Linear or seif dunes run parallel to the dominant wind direction. In coastal environments, sand forms dunes as it accumulates around obstacles, especially vegetation such as marram grass and sea couch grass. Coastal dunes form ridges that run parallel to the coastline.

e.g. the Great Erg in the Sahara Desert; Ainsdale dunes on the Merseyside coast near Southport.

dyke: minor *igneous intrusion* that cuts vertically through surrounding older rocks.

Because dykes crop out over a relatively small area, they have only a limited impact on the landscape. However, they often occur in large numbers or 'swarms', radiating out from a much larger igneous intrusion. Dolerite is the most common rock that forms dykes. Because dolerite is a resistant rock, it often forms narrow ridge-like features just a few metres high.

e.g. the Cleveland Dyke of Tertiary age, which originates in Mull in western Scotland and extends through southern Scotland and northern England as far as the North York Moors.

TIP Don't confuse dykes with *sills*, which are also a type of minor igneous intrusion. Dykes are vertical intrusions whereas sills are horizontal sheets of igneous rock.

earthquake: shock waves in the Earth's crust caused by the fracturing of rocks and their sudden movement along fault lines.

- Earthquakes occur most frequently along plate margins. The location of rock fracture within the crust is the focus, and the point at the surface directly above the focus is the earthquake epicentre. Earthquake magnitude is measured on the Richter scale. The destruction caused by earthquakes depends on earthquake magnitude, population density, building technology, the effectiveness of emergency procedures, etc.

- *e.g.* the Kobe earthquake in Japan in 1995, which measured 7.2 on the Richter scale.

economic man: assumption in classic economic models that decision-makers are perfectly informed, wholly rational and optimising in their behaviour (i.e. they aim either to maximise profits or to minimise costs).

- Because decision making is infinitely complex, the concept of economic man simplifies human behaviour and makes economic models operational. However, the concept is criticised as simplistic. An alternative approach argues that decision-makers are *satisficers* (rather than *optimisers*) and are often motivated by non-economic goals.

- *e.g.* decision-making in Weber's industrial location model (see *Weber's theory*), which defines the optimal location for a firm as one that minimises total transport costs.

- *TIP* The concept of economic man and the models and theories in which it figures have limited significance for modern economic geography. Current examination questions at AS and A-level give little prominence to these models per se.

economies of scale: see *internal* and *external economies of scale*.

ecosystem: community of living organisms and the physical environment.

- Ecosystems are driven by solar energy. This energy is transmitted from green plants to other organisms in ecosystems by a *food chain* or *food web*. Nutrients, such as carbon and nitrogen, cycle between the physical environment and living organisms. These energy and nutrient flows bind together the biotic (living) and abiotic (non-living) components of ecosystems. This interrelatedness gives ecosystems a holistic quality (i.e. the various parts function as a whole, so that change in one element produces change elsewhere).

- *e.g.* Ecosystems exist at all scales, from the continental to the local. The Amazon rainforest is a continental-scale ecosystem; the Morecambe Bay estuary is a local-scale ecosystem.

ecotourism: form of tourism based around ecological and human resources such as wildlife, scenic landscapes, traditional cultures and heritage.

- Ecotourism is the opposite of mass tourism. It caters for small visitor numbers and aims to make sustainable use of tourism resources.

- *e.g.* ecotourism in Costa Rica since the mid-1980s, based on sightseeing in rainforest, mountain and volcanic environments, and small-scale development around beach resorts.

- *TIP* Although ecotourism is more likely to be sustainable (see *sustainability*) than mass tourism, in some instances ecotourism has damaged fragile environments (e.g. scuba diving on coral reefs, safari tours in east Africa, footpath *erosion* in US National Parks).

edge city: city-like settlements on the fringes of existing urban settlements.

- Edge cities have developed in the USA where they mainly comprise socially and economically exclusive residential areas. They are often located close to shops, offices, business parks etc. that have decentralised from inner urban areas.

- *TIP* Edge cities should not be confused with the more general spread of urban development (housing, shopping centres, industrial estates, office parks etc.) in *rural–urban fringe* areas.

effective precipitation: amount of precipitation that is available for plant growth after losses to *evaporation*.

- Effective precipitation is a more accurate indicator of the hydrological potential of an area for crop growth than mean annual precipitation.

- *e.g.* Mean annual precipitation of 600 mm is likely to provide a more favourable environment for cropping in the UK than in north Africa. This is because the UK has much lower rates of evaporation, leaving more water available for crops.

ejecta: fragments of rock (e.g. pyroclasts) and ash thrown out by a volcanic explosion.

- Ejecta such as rock and ash particles are usually associated with viscous *magma*, which traps gases and leads to the build-up of high pressures. The result is violent volcanic eruptions.

- *e.g.* The Mount St Helen's eruption of 1980 released huge volumes of volcanic ash. Pyroclasts weighing 4 or 5 tonnes were blown several kilometres from the crater.

El Niño: name given to an unusually warm area of surface water around the equator in the eastern Pacific Ocean.

- On average, an El Niño event occurs every 3 years. These events cause major disruption to the world's weather. The high temperatures in the eastern Pacific (up to 8°C above average) result from the failure of the southeast trade winds, which normally push warm water westwards and allow cool water to well up off the coast of South America. The impact of El Niño includes: drought in the eastern Pacific; heavy *convectional precipitation* in the western Pacific; the disruption of marine *food chains* off the coast of Peru and Ecuador, leading to the collapse of local fisheries; reductions in crop yields; and floods and landslides.

ELR: see *environmental lapse rate*.

eluviation: process of downwashing soil particles (minerals, plant nutrients, humus) from surface to sub-surface horizons in the soil.

Eluviation is partly responsible for the development of the sandy, bleached Ea horizon in *podzol* soils. It also contributes to the extremely acidic environment of these soils.

TIP Eluviation is easily confused with *illuviation*. Whereas eluviation describes a removal of soil particles, illuviation is the opposite (i.e. an accumulation or washing-in of particles to sub-surface horizons).

emigration: out-migration of people from a place, which involves a permanent or semi-permanent change of residence.

Emigration often refers to the international movement of population. It is a selective process. Younger adults, single adults, the better educated, the more highly skilled etc. are more likely to migrate. Emigration may have adverse demographic, social and economic effects on the migrants' place of origin (e.g. ageing populations, unbalanced age and sex structures, depopulation, decline of local services).

e.g. Emigration from Ireland to the USA and Britain in the nineteenth century so depleted the country's population that in 1901 Ireland's total population (4.5 million) was 3.2 million less than in 1831.

TIP Note that emigration (i.e. out-migration) is the opposite of *immigration* (i.e. in-migration).

Enterprise Zone: UK planning unit devised in the 1980s, which covered areas of acute unemployment, dereliction and decay in towns and cities.

Between 1981 and 1984 the UK government created 23 Enterprise Zones (EZs). For a limited period (10 years) economic activities were given various incentives to locate in EZs, including exemption from local rates and corporation tax and simplified planning procedures. EZs were revived in the mid-1990s, when many hard-hit coalfield communities were given EZ status.

e.g. the Gateshead EZ, which attracted the Metro Centre, one of the UK's largest planned regional shopping centres.

environmental lapse rate (ELR): vertical distribution of temperature in the atmosphere at a given time.

The ELR varies from day to day, but averages 6.5°C per kilometre for the lower part of the atmosphere. This decrease in temperature with height (i.e. lapse rate) is mainly caused by the increase in distance from the main source of heat (the Earth's surface) and the lower density of the atmosphere at height, which means less efficient heat absorption and heat transfer.

▨ *TIP* There is much confusion concerning the ELR and adiabatic lapse rates (see *adiabatic cooling*). Remember that the ELR is simply the temperature of the atmosphere, at different heights, now. Adiabatic lapse rates, on the other hand, describe how the temperature of a rising air parcel changes with height.

Environmentally Sensitive Area (ESA): areas of countryside in the UK where farmers receive payments from government to protect the landscape and wildlife by using traditional farming methods.

▨ Most ESAs are in the uplands. The distinctive landscapes and wildlife in ESAs are the result of traditional farming methods practised over hundreds of years. Modern methods such as the use of chemical fertilisers, sown grasses and silage are more cost effective, but threaten the environment. The money paid to farmers in ESAs is compensation for the lower profits yielded by traditional methods.

▨ *e.g.* ESAs in Swaledale, which help conserve species-rich hay meadows and rare plants such as butterfly orchids and white frog orchids.

equinox: 2 days in the year (21 March and 22 September) when the sun's rays strike the plane of Earth's axis at right angles.

▨ At the equinoxes, the sun is above the horizon for exactly 12 hours everywhere (apart from the Poles) and is directly overhead at the equator at noon.

eroded anticline: simple symmetrical upfolded structure where the younger rocks have been removed by erosion, exposing older rocks near the centre of the axis of folding.

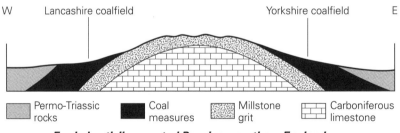

Eroded anticline: central Pennines, northern England

▨ Eroded anticlines often have inward-facing *escarpments* of more resistant rocks. The stripping away of younger rocks from the central part of the fold is due to cracking at the surface along the major fold axis, exposing this area to *erosion*.

▨ *e.g.* the Wealden anticline in Sussex and Kent, flanked by the inward-facing escarpments of the chalk North and South Downs.

erosion: wearing away of the land surface and the removal of weathered rock debris by rivers, *glaciers*, waves and wind.

▨ *TIP* Refer to the entry for *weathering* and make sure that you understand the difference between erosion and weathering.

erratic: rock particle transported by *ice sheets* and *glaciers* which is of different geology to the country rocks of the area in which it has been deposited.

▓ Erratics are an important source of evidence of ice movement during the Pleistocene.

▓ *e.g.* Shap granite erratics from the eastern edge of the Lake District, which are found in Lancashire, Cheshire and the Tees Valley.

ESA: see *Environmentally Sensitive Area.*

escarpment (also called 'cuesta'): tilt block forming an extensive upland area.

▓ Escarpments have a short, steep *scarp slope* and a long, gentle *dip slope*. They owe their form to (a) folding on a regional scale and (b) their resistance to *erosion* compared to surrounding rocks. Escarpments form the most prominent relief features in eastern and southeast England.

▓ *e.g.* the Cotswolds in Gloucestershire, formed from Oolitic limestone.

esker: long, sinuous ridge made of *glacio-fluvial deposits* such as sand and gravel.

▓ Eskers represent the channel deposits of powerful sub-glacial and englacial meltwater streams. Their meandering planform clearly shows their fluvial origin. Eskers, along with other glacio-fluvial landforms, developed during *deglaciation* at the close of the last *glacial*.

estuary: tidal, funnel-shaped river mouth along a lowland coast.

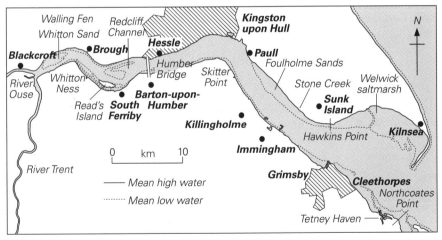

The Humber Estuary, draining one fifth of England and over 100 km long

▓ Estuaries are former lowland river valleys submerged by the eustatic rise in sea level between 20,000 and 6,000 BP (see *glacio-eustacy*). Estuaries are sediment sinks. In the last 6,000 years, rapid sediment *accretion* (from fluvial and marine sources) within estuaries has formed *mudflats* and *salt marshes*. This infilling, together with strong tidal currents, gives estuaries their distinctive funnel-shaped planform.

▓ *e.g.* Estuaries with classic funnel-shapes include the Severn and the Thames.

▓ *TIP* Taking account of the physical processes operating in estuaries (e.g. tidal scour, *tidal range*, river sediment loads etc.), you should consider why some river mouths are estuaries and others are deltas.

ethnic segregation: see *segregation*.

eutrophication: depletion of oxygen from water in streams and rivers.

▓ Water enrichment caused by pollution (e.g. from nitrates from intensive agriculture or untreated sewage) results in the rapid growth of algae and bacteria. Their demand for oxygen lowers oxygen levels in the river, suffocating aquatic life such as insects, molluscs and fish.

evaporation: phase change of water from liquid to gas.

▓ Evaporation is the main pathway by which water re-enters the atmosphere. Rates of evaporation depend on temperature, *humidity* and wind speed. Evaporation requires energy and removes heat from a surface. This latent heat is later released in condensation. Evaporation is an important factor in river basin hydrology and in soil moisture availability to plants.

evapotranspiration: combined water loss from a surface through *evaporation* and *transpiration* from plants.

▓ Actual evapotranspiration depends on the availability of moisture in the soil. It is difficult to measure and of limited value. Potential evapotranspiration assumes that water is always available and is a more effective instrument for assessing the *water balance* and the suitability of an area for cropping.

exfoliation: peeling away of the outer layers of rock surfaces.

▓ Exfoliation is the outcome of both *chemical* and *physical weathering* (including *pressure release*) processes. It often produces boulders and rock outcrops with smooth, rounded forms.

▓ *TIP* Exfoliation is not in itself a weathering process. It describes the way in which some rocks disintegrate as a result of chemical and physical weathering.

exfoliation dome: large, domed rock outcrop that owes its form to *exfoliation*.

▓ *Pressure release*, particularly in granitic areas, is mainly responsible for the development of exfoliation domes.

▓ *e.g.* exfoliation domes in the Sierra Nevada in the Yosemite National Park, California.

▓ *TIP* Although similar in appearance to *bornhardts*, *tors* and castle kopjes, exfoliation domes result from different processes. While exfoliation domes owe their form to pressure release, bornhardts, tors and castle kopjes have been shaped by sub-surface *chemical weathering* under humid tropical conditions.

extending flow: type of internal flow in *glaciers* characterised by a downward component of ice movement along slip lines.

▓ Extending flow occurs above the firnline (see diagram on page 26) and in areas where there is an increase in flow velocity and/or gradient.

▓ *e.g.* the internal flow of ice in a *cirque* from the headwall to the floor zone.

external economies of scale: savings made by a firm that arise from outside the firm itself.

■ There are two kinds of external economy: localisation economies and *urbanisation economies*. Clusters of firms interlinked in the production chain derive benefits from geographical proximity (e.g. easier contact and exchanges of information, transport savings, shorter delivery times). Urbanisation economies are the advantages to a firm of the *infrastructure* already provided in large urban areas (e.g. roads, utilities, housing for workers).

■ *e.g.* Hundreds of small businesses making leather goods, clothing, textiles, ceramics etc. in Emilia-Romagna in northern Italy gain important localisation economies by clustering.

■ *TIP* External economies are quite separate from *internal economies*. Read the entry for internal economies and note the difference.

externalities: side-effects or spill-over effects of an economic activity on the physical environment, neighbouring populations and society.

■ Externalities may be positive or negative. Negative externalities are that part of the cost of production that is passed on, at least in part, by an economic activity to the environment and society.

■ *e.g.* Jobs created by a quarry for local people are a positive externality. The impact of the quarry on the surrounding area — noise, dust, loss of visual amenity etc. — is a negative externality.

exurbs: settlements that are functionally linked to nearby urban areas, but which are physically separate from them.

■ Unlike the suburbs, the exurbs are not contiguous with a large urban area. Many exurban settlements are commuter or dormitory villages. The people living in the exurbs rely on the nearby town or city for employment and services. In this sense, they are functionally (though not physically) attached to the nearby town or city.

■ *e.g.* the commuter villages of north Warwickshire, which form part of the exurbs of the West Midlands conurbation.

family cycle: idea that most individuals pass through a number of distinct family-centred stages during their lives.

■ These stages include young single adults, young couples without children, older couples with children, older couples whose children have left home etc. At each stage, individuals and families have different housing needs (space, garden, access to schools etc.). Thus the stage in the family cycle has a strong influence on where people live.

■ *e.g.* Young singles may choose to live in apartments close to the city centre with good access to services (clubs, bars, restaurants, cinemas etc.). Couples with young children may opt for more spacious housing in the suburbs, with a garden and access to good schools.

fault: rock fracture, caused by movements in the Earth's crust.

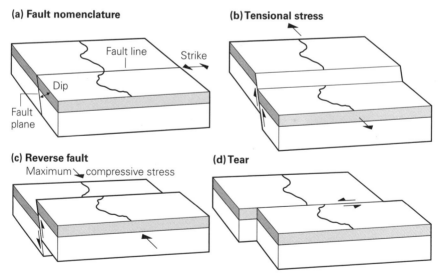

Major types of fault: (a) illustration of dip, strike, fault line and fault plane; (b) normal fault; (c) reverse fault; (d) tear fault

■ Faults extend across bedding planes and pseudo-bedding planes (see *pressure release*) and normally there is some displacement along the fault line. There are two simple types of fault: a normal fault caused by tension; and a reverse fault caused by compression. The angle of the fault line from the horizontal is the dip, the vertical displacement is the throw, and the lateral displacement is the heave.

 e.g. the Highland boundary fault, which marks the northern boundary of the midland valley of central Scotland.

 TIP Faults and *joints* are easily confused. Joints are usually smaller-scale fractures, confined to a single rock layer in sedimentary rocks, or the result of contraction cooling or unloading (see *pressure release*) in massive igneous rocks. There is no displacement along joints.

fault-line scarp: steep slope that extends for several kilometres parallel to a fault line, and which marks the edge of a plateau or *escarpment*.

 Fault-line scarps are usually older than *fault scarps* and have been eroded back from the fault line. However, they have retained their original steep angle.

 e.g. Malham Cove, 1 km north of the Mid-Craven fault in north Yorkshire.

fault scarp: steep slope that extends for several kilometres along a fault line and marks the edge of a plateau or *escarpment*.

 Fault scarps mark the actual line of the fault in the landscape. The fault scarp may be the result of either normal faulting or reverse faulting.

 e.g. the Teton fault scarp in Wyoming; the North Pennine fault scarp.

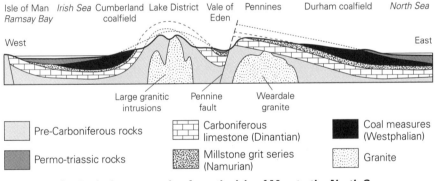

Geological cross-section from the Isle of Man to the North Sea showing the North Pennine fault scarp

FDI: see *foreign direct investment.*

fertility: number of children born in a population in a year, or the average number of children born to each woman during her lifetime.

 There are several measures of fertility. Total fertility is the average number of children born to each woman during her lifetime; age-specific fertility is the average number of children born to women of a given age in a year; general fertility is the average number of children born to women in the 15–45 age group in a year. The *crude birth rate* (CBR) is the most common index of fertility. However, the strong influence of age structure on the CBR makes it the least accurate measure.

TIP Fertility in a demographic sense is not the same as the ability to have children. Demographers refer to the latter as fecundity.

fetch: distance of open sea or ocean over which waves are generated.

Usually the longer the fetch, the more powerful the waves. Thus fetch is an important factor influencing rates of coastal *erosion*.

TIP Fetch can be measured in any direction from a coastal location. However, fetch is usually taken to mean the maximum distance of open sea or ocean over which waves are generated. Waves generated by this fetch have the greatest impact on the coastal system.

field capacity: maximum amount of water that soil can hold against the pull of gravity.

The date of return of the soil to field capacity is important to agriculture. It indicates the time when drains begin to run and after which heavy rainfall is likely to cause flooding. After the return date, the land becomes unworkable.

e.g. In an average year in north Norfolk, the soil is at field capacity from 1 December to 2 April.

TIP You should make connections between field capacity, saturated *overland flow* and stream discharge.

firn: compacted snow that has recrystallised into a denser granular ice.

Firn has a density greater than 0.55, compared with 0.1 for snow and 0.89 for glacier ice.

fissure: see *vent*.

fjord: *glacial trough* drowned by the post-glacial rise in sea level.

Fjords are found in middle to high latitudes where glaciated uplands are adjacent to the coast. They are typically long, branching and steep-sided. As a result of intense glacial *erosion*, fjords are also deep. However, they become shallow towards their seaward end. Here glacial erosion was less intense as the glacier met the sea and began to float.

e.g. the Sognefjord in southern Norway which, 100 km from the sea, is nearly 1 km deep.

flexible production: opposite production strategy to *mass production*, where firms specialise in the production of small runs of customised goods.

Flexible production is driven by customer demand and requires manufacturers to respond quickly to changes in the market.

e.g. car manufacturers making models with hundreds of different specifications.

flood: when river discharge exceeds *bankfull* capacity, and water spills out of a river channel and inundates surrounding areas.

Wild rivers (i.e. those unregulated by human activities) may flood on average once or twice a year. There are two general causes of flooding: excessive *precipitation*; and the rapid movement of water into stream and river channels. Floods occur in winter when *evapotranspiration* is low, soils are either saturated or frozen and there is little interception from vegetation; in spring when snow melts; and in summer following torrential thunderstorms ('flash' floods).

■ *e.g.* the floods in Mozambique in 2000, following several weeks of heavy precipitation.

■ *TIP* Floods are one of the most common natural hazards and a favourite subject for examination questions. You should study one or more flood events and focus on the causes of flooding, the impact of flooding and the resulting human responses.

flood control: attempt to confine flood waters to river channels or regulate runoff and prevent extreme flows.

■ Flood control aims to reduce the risk to people and property on *flood plains*. It would be largely unnecessary if flood plains were unoccupied. Flood waters may be confined to river channels by building *levées*, widening and deepening river channels, straightening river channels, constructing relief channels, etc. Flows can be regulated by building dams in the headwaters, installing sluice gates across a river and storing floodwater in washland areas, and managing land use (e.g. *afforestation*) in the catchment. Other approaches include zoning land use on flood plains and early warning to evacuate people when flooding is imminent.

■ *e.g.* dams on the River Rhône in France which, apart from regulating the river's flow and providing flood protection, also generate *hydro-electric power* and improve navigation.

flood plain: wide, flat floor of a river valley infilled with *alluvium*.

■ Flood plains are the result of fluvial erosion and fluvial deposition. Lateral erosion widens out the valley floor. This area is filled with alluvium, which includes coarse sand, gravel and fine silt. Alluvium comes from two sources: (a) channel deposits, comprising *point bars* and channel bars; and (b) *overbank deposits*, which mainly comprise the fine silt carried as suspended *load*.

■ *e.g.* the Severn Valley, near Tewkesbury.

fog: tiny droplets of water (or ice) suspended in the free air and reaching ground level, which restrict visibility to less than 1 km.

■ Fog forms when humid air near the ground is cooled to its dew-point, and a gentle breeze spreads this cooling some distance above surface. The two types of fog — *radiation fog* and *advection fog* — have different cooling mechanisms. Radiation fog forms when long-wave radiation from the ground at night cools the overlying air. Advection fog forms when relatively warm air moves horizontally over a cooler surface and is chilled to its *dew-point*. Radiation fog only forms over the land; advection fog most commonly forms at sea and in coastal areas, hence its alternative name — sea fog.

■ *e.g.* Advection fog is particularly frequent along the North Sea coast between the Humber and the Firth of Tay. In Scotland it is known locally as the 'haar'. In northeast England the term 'sea fret' is used.

■ *TIP* You may come across several other kinds of fog (e.g. ground fog, ice fog, supercooled fog). However, they are all types of radiation or advection fog. You should also note that the only difference between fog and *stratus cloud* is that fog extends down to ground level. Stratus cloud at ground level in upland areas is known as hill fog.

föhn wind: warm, dry wind that descends the leeward slopes of high mountains and produces a dramatic rise in temperature in adjacent lowlands.

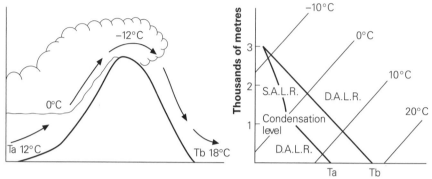

Ta refers to the temperature at the windward foot of the range, and Tb to that at the leeward foot.

The föhn effect when an air parcel is forced to cross a mountain range

▩ Föhn winds are caused when an airstream rises over a mountain barrier, cools and forms clouds. Cooling on the windward side is at the lower saturated adiabatic lapse rate (SALR) (see *adiabatic cooling*). Once the airstream has shed its moisture and descends, it heats up at the higher dry adiabatic lapse rate (DALR). This means that, at the same altitude, temperatures on the leeward side are higher than those on the windward side. This heating is known as the föhn effect.

▩ *e.g.* The wind that gave its name to the föhn effect blows north from the Swiss Alps to the Swiss Plateau. The Chinook (literally 'snow eater') in Alberta is also a föhn wind.

folding: pressure within the Earth's crust that causes layered rocks to bend rather than fracture.

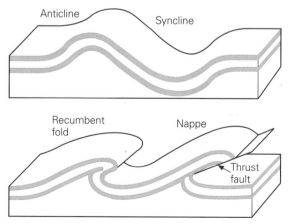

Basic types of fold structures

▓ Folded structures have an axis, which is the hinge line where the sides of the fold change their angle of dip. The sides of the fold are called limbs. The simplest folds are symmetrical around their axes. A symmetrical upfold is an anticline; a symmetrical downfold is a *syncline*. When lateral pressure increases, fold structures become more complex. A fold pushed on its side is known as a *recumbent fold*. Extreme pressure may cause the upper part of a fold to shear along a thrust fault. The strata pushed forward along this thrust fault are called a *nappe*.

food chain (also called 'food web'): series of organisms through which food energy moves before it is completely expended.

▓ Solar energy is captured by green plants through *photosynthesis*. The autotrophs are the primary producers of energy in an ecosystem. Food energy is transferred from plants to primary consumers or herbivores, and from herbivores to carnivores (secondary and tertiary consumers). In this way, energy is moved along a food chain or through a food web. Ultimately, dead organic material is consumed by detritivores such as soil bacteria and fungi.

▓ *e.g.* the transfer of food energy from oak leaves (primary producers), to caterpillars (primary consumers), blue tits (secondary consumers) and sparrowhawks (tertiary consumers).

▓ *TIP* A food chain represents a simplified movement of energy in an *ecosystem*. In reality, energy moves through complex food webs. In food webs, several organisms occupy the same niche, are both herbivorous and carnivorous, and may feed on secondary, tertiary and quaternary consumers.

food web: see *food chain*.

footloose industry: industry that has few constraints on its location.

▓ Footloose industries are mainly light industries making products with high added value. They are little affected in their choice of location by traditional factors such as energy, transport and raw materials.

▓ *e.g. high-tech industries*.

▓ *TIP* It would be wrong to think that footloose industries can locate anywhere. Many footloose industries form distinct clusters, which suggests they are subject to locational constraints. For instance, many high-tech industries are geographically concentrated near to universities, research institutions, venture capital, international airports and areas of high environmental quality (in order to attract highly skilled and highly paid workers).

foreign aid: assistance given by a foreign government, an international body or a non-governmental organisation (NGO) to an LEDC.

▓ Foreign aid may comprise gifts of money, goods and services. In emergencies (e.g. famines, floods), short-term aid such as medicines, tents, blankets and food may be given. Long-term aid may be for economic development (e.g. irrigation for agriculture, energy production) or social development (e.g. education, health, family planning). *Bilateral aid* is assistance given by one country directly to another. Multilateral aid is assistance given to poor countries by international bodies such as the United Nations and World Bank. Tied aid has conditions attached that benefit the donor as well as the receiver.

■ *e.g.* The UK's controversial funding of the Pergau Dam in Malaysia was linked to an arms contract that tied Malaysia to the purchase of military equipment from the UK.

foreign direct investment (FDI): inward investment by a foreign company (usually a large *transnational corporation*) in a country or region.

▓ FDI is sought by governments in both LEDCs and MEDCs. Currently 60% of all FDI goes to MEDCs. In the EU, the UK has been highly successful in attracting FDI from the USA and east Asia since the mid-1980s. Governments offer incentives such as grants and loans to TNCs to secure inward investment.

■ *e.g.* Toyota's new car plant at Valenciennes in northern France, due to open in 2001.

■ *TIP* You should be aware that FDI has disadvantages as well as advantages for a country or region. The advantages include job creation, the introduction of new technologies, and a positive contribution to the balance of trade. The main disadvantage is external control and future disinvestment (see *branch plant*).

fossil fuels: fuels such as oil, natural gas, coal and peat derived from the fossilised remains of plants and animals.

▓ The economically developed world has relied on fossil fuels as its main source of energy for the last 200 years. Fossil fuels are *non-renewable resources* and their use is directly responsible for a number of environmental problems including climate change or *global warming*. Contemporary industrialisation in LEDCs such as China and India is based on fossil fuels.

▓ *e.g.* At a local scale, the extraction of coal through either deep-mining or *open-casting* causes environmental problems. Former coalfields such as south Wales and Durham still show the environmental scars of deep-mining. The detrimental environmental impact of open-casting is currently a sensitive issue in areas such as Northumberland and Derbyshire.

■ *TIP* You should clarify your views on the world's continued dependence on fossil fuels, i.e. your priorities — economic advantages/environmental dis-advantages.

Friedmann's core–periphery model: four-stage model of development where development is initially concentrated in the economic *core* and eventually diffuses into the *periphery*.

▓ The model suggests that, in the early stages of development, wide regional disparities between core and periphery emerge. During this time the periphery is in a position of dependency, and lags behind the core. A single primate city (see *primacy*) dominates the country's settlement hierarchy. As the country's economy expands, the economies of the core and periphery converge. A mature hierarchy of cities emerges characterised by a smooth city-size distri-bution (see *rank-size distribution*).

Stage 1 Relatively independent local centres; no hierarchy. Typical pre-industrial structure; each city lies at the centre of a small regional enclave.

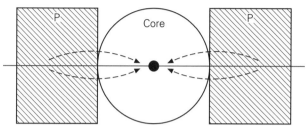

Stage 2 A single strong core. Typical of period of incipient industrialisation; a periphery emerges; potential entrepreneurs and labour move to the core; national economy is virtually reduced to a single metropolitan region.

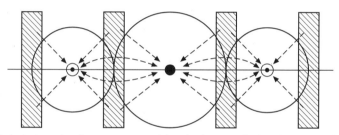

Stage 3 A single national core, strong peripheral sub-cores. During the period of industrial maturity, secondary cores form, thereby reducing the periphery on a national scale to smaller intermetropolitan peripheries.

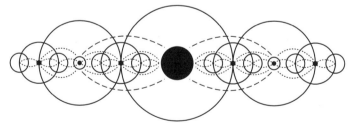

Stage 4 A functional interdependent system of cities. Organised complexity characterised by national integration, efficiency in location, maximum growth potential.

Friedmann's core–periphery model

■ ***TIP*** Remember that Friedmann's ideas are theoretical and can be challenged. In fact, there is little evidence to prove the convergence of core and periphery economies. The EU has the oldest industrialised countries in the world, yet regional inequalities remain between the economic core (e.g. Paris, Frankfurt, London) and the economic periphery (e.g. Greece, Portugal, northwest Scotland).

front: boundary that separates two *airmasses* in a *depression*.

■ There are three main types of front: *warm, cold* and occluded (see *occlusion*).

All three are found in depressions and are associated with rising air, extensive bands of cloud and prolonged *precipitation*.

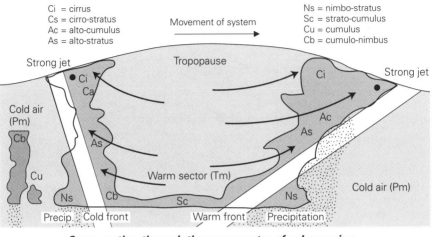

Cross-section through the warm sector of a depression

frost: air or ground temperature at or below freezing.

The term 'frost' has several meanings. An air frost is a zero or sub-zero temperature above the ground surface, and occurs less often than a ground frost. Hoar frost is the white crystalline deposit that forms on vegetation and other surfaces when temperatures fall to zero and below zero at the ground.

TIP In common usage, frost usually means hoar frost. However, in a strict meteorological sense, frost refers to temperatures at and below freezing. It is this meaning that is most likely to be examined at AS and A-level.

frost heave: the net downslope displacement that occurs when the soil, during a freeze–thaw cycle, expands normal to the surface, and settles in a nearly vertical direction.

Frost heave is an important process in *gelifluction* and *solifluction*. It causes a downslope movement of *regolith* known as frost creep. The freezing of saturated regolith leads to the formation of ice crystals which can push stones and loose debris towards the surface.

frost weathering: form of *physical weathering* where water, trapped in rock joints and rock pores, freezes, expands and causes the mechanical breakdown of rocks.

Frost wedging describes the effect of frost action in joints in impermeable rocks. This process leads to block disintegration on massively jointed rocks, and the formation of scree-sized particles on densely jointed rocks. Frost shattering is the effect of frost on porous rocks such as chalk, where water is trapped in tiny pore spaces between mineral particles.

e.g. Features such as *blockfields* and *scree slopes* are evidence of frost wedging. In the UK, most of these landforms are relict features and are no longer active today.

■ *TIP* An approach to frost weathering favoured by examiners is to investigate your understanding of the factors that determine the effectiveness of frost weathering. The obvious factors (sub-zero temperatures, plenty of moisture) are well known. What is often forgotten is the crucial role of freeze–thaw cycles (i.e. the number of occasions when temperatures fluctuate above and below freezing).

gelifluction: slow downslope flow of saturated *regolith* resting on a layer of *permafrost*.

■ Gelifluction is a mass movement that is widespread in *periglacial environments*. Although it is predominantly a flow process, it also includes *frost heave* (see *mass movement*). It can occur on slopes of just one or two degrees and gives rise to landforms such as gelifluction sheets, lobes, stone-banked and earth-banked terraces.

gentrification: processes by which former low-income inner-city housing areas in MEDCs are invaded by higher-income groups and refurbished.

■ Gentrification occurs because living in the inner city gives easy access to services and employment in the CBD. It is a form of *reurbanisation*.

■ *e.g.* inner London districts such as Islington and Clapham.

■ *TIP* It is worth remembering that gentrification is unusual because it runs counter to the general decentralisation that dominated population movements in most cities in MEDCs in the second half of the twentieth century.

geo: long, narrow inlet on a cliffed coastline.

■ Geos are relatively small-scale features, formed by roof collapse in a sea cave that runs at right angles to the shoreline.

■ *e.g.* Huntsman's Leap, Pembrokeshire.

geostrophic wind: balanced wind that blows at high level in the *troposphere*, parallel to the *isobars*.

■ The geostrophic wind is the outcome of the balance of two forces: the *pressure gradient* force and the *Coriolis force*. Near the Earth's surface a third factor — friction — modifies the geostrophic wind, causing it to blow at a slight angle to the isobars.

ghetto: concentration of people of similar socio-economic or cultural or ethnic background within a well-defined geographical enclave in a city.

■ In medieval Europe, the original ghettos were walled enclaves that accommodated the Jewish minority. Ghettos developed for protection and to preserve a group's cultural identity. In modern cities, ghettos are often synonymous with slums and poverty.

■ *e.g.* the predominantly black inner-city area of Watts in Los Angeles.

■ *TIP* Try to distinguish clearly between the concepts of ghettos and slums. For many people, ghettos may represent a positive choice of where to live in the city. In contrast, people living in slums rarely do so out of choice.

glacial: prolonged period of cooling of the Earth's climate, causing continental-scale glaciation.

■ Glacial conditions have been the norm for 90% of the past 2 million years.

■ *e.g.* The most recent glacial — the Devensian — lasted for most of the past 100,000 years. Ice sheets covered most of northern Britain, East Anglia, Wales and Ireland.

■ *TIP* Don't imagine that glaciation was uniform in the last 100,000 years. There were times when ice buried even the highest peaks in the British Isles (e.g. in the late Devensian, 26,000 years BP). At other times, the highest ground was exposed. During warmer spells, glaciation was confined to valley *glaciers* in the uplands.

glacial outwash: sands and gravels deposited by meltwater.

■ Glacial outwash is the debris produced by glacial *erosion* and *weathering*, transported and deposited by meltwater streams. It forms stratified deposits, and *glacio-fluvial* landforms such as *eskers*, *kames* and *sandar* (outwash plains).

■ *e.g.* the huge area of glacial outwash deposited along the coast of southeast Iceland.

■ *TIP* Glacial outwash deposits differ from other glacial deposits because they are layered. This tells you that they were laid down by streams and rivers, and not directly by melting or moving ice.

glacial trough: another name for U-shaped glacial valley.

■ Glacial troughs are found in glaciated uplands. They are characteristically steep-sided and flat-floored. Overdeepening of glacial troughs causes tributary valleys to hang above the main valley. Spurs are truncated, and the head of the valley often ends abruptly in a steep rock wall or *trough head*.

■ *e.g.* Lauterbrunnen Valley, Switzerland.

■ *TIP* Glacial troughs are occupied by small valley *glaciers* in high mountain ranges such as the Alps and Himalayas today. However, it is unlikely that these glaciers were responsible for excavating glacial troughs. Most were probably cut by fast-flowing *ice streams* during periods of continental glaciation.

glacier: body of ice showing evidence of movement such as flowlines and crevasses.

■ Glaciers form where the rate of snow accumulation exceeds the rate of *ablation*. The difference between accumulation and ablation is the *mass balance* of the glacier. Today glaciers are confined to polar environments and high mountains. Polar glaciers are the largest and most stable and include the Antarctic and Greenland *ice sheets*. Smaller bodies of ice found in high plateau areas are known as *icefields* (e.g. Columbia icefield). Alpine (or valley) glaciers are much smaller. They exist in warmer climates and are restricted to mountainous areas such as the Alps, Himalayas and Andes. Cirque glaciers are the smallest glaciers: confined to *cirque* basins, they form where annual accumulation just exceeds ablation. Several decades of net accumulation will cause cirque glaciers to advance beyond the cirque basin to form alpine (valley) glaciers.

glacier movement: *glaciers* move by flowing and sliding.

Although glacier ice is solid and brittle, it can flow under stress. A glacier also moves by sliding on its bed. This sliding process is most important in warm-based alpine glaciers, where meltwater acts as a lubricant. The speed of flow depends on gradient and temperature. Where the flow speed is variable (e.g. ice falls and valley bends), crevasses develop.

e.g. The Nisqually glacier on Mount Rainier is a warm-based alpine (valley) glacier. About 5–20% of its movement is due to flow; 80–95% is due to basal sliding. In summer, its flow rate has been measured at nearly 50 cm a day. The winter flow rate is around 20 cm a day.

TIP Glacier movement has important implications for glacial erosion and the development of landforms. Ice that is frozen to the surface (i.e. cold-based glaciers) will move by flowing, and may protect the surface from *erosion*. Warm-based glaciers that slide along their bed will accomplish high rates of erosion through *abrasion* and *quarrying*.

glacio-eustacy: worldwide changes in sea level caused by *glacial* and *inter-glacial* periods.

During a glacial, water accumulates as ice in *glaciers*, sea level falls (by around 100 m) and the coastline advances. In warmer inter-glacials, shrinking *ice sheets* and glaciers produce a rise in sea level of similar magnitude. Rising sea level leads to the retreat of coastlines, their submergence and the formation of *rias*, *fjords* and *estuaries*.

e.g. The present day inter-glacial (Holocene) period is one of high sea levels. Sea level stabilised around 6,000 years ago. The rise in sea level between 20,000 and 6,000 BP (the Flandrian transgression) flooded much of the continental shelf around the British Isles.

TIP It is important to appreciate that, because of sea level change in the last 20,000 years, our coastline and its features are relatively young. Thus many coastal erosional landforms (e.g. *shore platforms*) are relict features, which may have formed during previous inter-glacials. Meanwhile, depositional landforms such as *spits*, sand *dunes* and *salt marshes* cannot be more than 6,000 years old.

glacio-fluvial deposits: sands and gravels deposited by meltwater.

Glacio-fluvial deposits are associated with *deglaciation* and include landforms such as *sandar*, *kames* and *eskers*.

TIP Glacio-fluvial features are stratified or sorted by size. In contrast, sorting is absent in materials deposited by moving or melting ice (i.e. *moraines*).

glacio-isostacy: localised and relative change in sea level caused by the crust's response to loading and unloading of ice.

■ In *glacials*, ice loads the land and depresses the crust. When the ice melts (in *inter-glacials*), the crust rebounds (isostatic recovery) and rises. If this rise exceeds the rise in sea level, features such as *raised beaches* may form.

■ *e.g.* the extensive raised beaches in northwest Scotland (e.g. the Applecross Peninsula). The older beaches are 25 m above sea level; the more recent are 8 m above sea level. Isostatic recovery is particularly evident in northwest Scotland, which had the greatest thickness of ice during the last glacial.

gley soil: type of soil that is waterlogged for much of the year.

■ Oxygen is in short supply in waterlogged soils. As a result, iron is reduced to ferrous iron, giving gley soils a distinctive bluish-grey coloration. Waterlogging may be due to either a high water table (a groundwater gley) or an impermeable layer that impedes drainage (a surface water gley).

global energy budget: transfer of surplus energy in the tropics to the poles by winds and ocean currents.

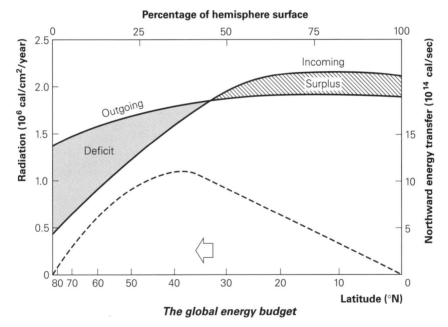

The global energy budget

■ The Earth-atmosphere system has a positive energy balance between 0 and 40 degrees of latitude. In this area, incoming solar radiation exceeds outgoing radiation from the Earth. Polewards of 40 degrees latitude, the Earth-atmosphere energy budget is in deficit (i.e. outgoing radiation exceeds incoming radiation). As a result of these global energy imbalances, energy is transported polewards by winds (80%) and warm ocean currents (20%). This global energy transfer is responsible for the atmosphere's general circulation, and for storms such as *hurricanes* and *depressions*.

globalisation: location of manufacturing and services by *transnational corporations* in several different countries or continents.

- The purpose of globalisation is for firms to source cheaper materials and labour, and to make products and supply services and markets worldwide.
- *e.g.* the growth of the software industry in Bangalore, India, to supply markets worldwide.
- *TIP* Globalisation is not confined to manufacturing industry. Many service activities currently based in MEDCs are looking to lower their costs by transferring their operations to LEDCs. Information technology and modern telecommunications make this possible.

global shift: increase in proportion of global manufacturing originating from LEDCs in the last 30 years.

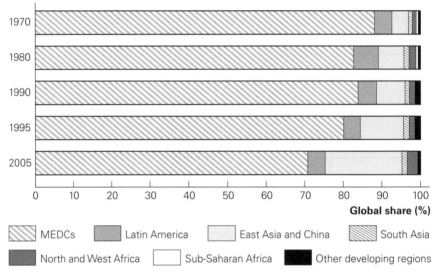

Changing regional shares of global manufacturing: 1970–2005

- The global shift is a consequence of *globalisation* and the increasing attraction of LEDCs for *foreign direct investment* by *transnational corporations*.
- *e.g.* the rapid *industrialisation* of the Pearl River delta region of eastern China. The driving force has been inward investment from companies based in Hong Kong and Taiwan. Industries are *labour-intensive* (textiles, clothing, toys, electronic equipment, etc.) and the main attraction is low labour costs.
- *TIP* Despite its name, the global shift does not mean the relocation of factories from MEDCs to LEDCs. The global shift has occurred largely because of an increase of foreign direct investment in LEDCs.

global warming: rise in average global temperatures over the last 200 years.

- In the twentieth century, average global temperatures increased by 0.6°C. Six of the ten warmest years on record occurred in the 1990s. Current forecasts suggest that global temperatures will increase by at least 1.6°C by 2100. One theory of global warming is that it is due to the burning of *fossil fuels* and rising levels of carbon dioxide in the atmosphere. This has a so-called *greenhouse effect*.

Global warming will bring significant economic and environmental disbenefits, including climate change and coastal flooding.

▓ *TIP* You should know that: (a) not all climatologists believe that global warming is due to the greenhouse effect (some argue that global warming is a natural fluctuation in global temperatures) and (b) the impact of global warming will be geographically uneven, with some parts of the world even experiencing a climatic cooling.

graben: valley formed by downfaulting between parallel *faults*.

▓ Graben (also known as rift valleys) are formed by tension in the Earth's crust. They are most common along *constructive plate boundaries*, where rifting is associated with earthquake and volcanic activity.

▓ *e.g.* Thingvellir in Iceland, formed by rifting along the margins of the Eurasian and North American plates.

graded profile: concave profile of a river in cross-section from its source to its mouth.

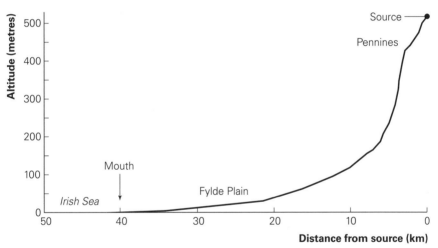

Graded, long profile of the River Wyre, Lancashire

▓ Given sufficient time and environmental stability, a river should develop a smooth, graded, concave profile. A graded profile is an equilibrium form. Discharge and channel efficiency increase downstream. This results in increased *erosion*, which reduces the average gradient. Eventually the increase in discharge and channel efficiency is everywhere balanced by the reduction in gradient. The river, after transporting its water and sediment, has no surplus energy. The outcome is a graded profile.

▓ *TIP* Be aware that all environmental processes (in this case tectonic and climatic) are dynamic, and rarely constant for long periods of time. Thus most rivers are unlikely to achieve truly graded profiles.

gravity model: type of interaction model that forecasts the movement of people, goods and ideas between two places.

The gravity model assumes that interaction is directly proportional to the size (or attractiveness) of two places, and inversely proportional to the distance between them.

$$I_{ij} = {}^{k}\left[\frac{P_i \times P_j}{D_{ij}{}^{n}}\right]$$

where I_{ij} = interaction between places i and j

P = measure of attractiveness of places i and j (usually population)

D_{ij} = measurement of distance (or time or cost) between i and j

n = distance exponent

k = constant or scaling factor

Gravity models are widely used in planning to forecast traffic flows. However, the simple form of the model (above) takes no account of competition from other places (see *Huff's interaction model*), and behavioural factors (e.g. *perception*) that influence *migration* and other population movements.

green belt: zone of predominantly rural land use encircling an urban area, where strict controls on development apply.

In the UK, the green belt idea is the standard planning device to limit *urban sprawl*. Green belts do not stop urban development: they simply interrupt it. Unable to expand in the suburbs, urban development leapfrogs the green belt to form *exurbs*. Green belts have been criticised for protecting poor-quality farmland near cities at the expense of higher-quality land beyond the green belt, benefiting higher-income groups who can afford housing on the edge of the city and encouraging long-distance commuting.

e.g. the green belt around London, which since the 1940s has effectively stopped the outward, contiguous growth of the capital.

TIP The green belt is only one device used by planners to control urban sprawl. Elsewhere in Europe, alternatives such as green wedges (Copenhagen), buffer zones (Randstad) and green axes (Paris) have proved more flexible.

greenfield site: site for housing, commerce or industry that has not previously been built on.

Greenfield sites are usually located on the edge of town, often in *green belt* areas zoned for non-urban land use. For this reason, their development is frequently controversial. Greenfield sites are generally preferred to *brownfield sites* because they are easier to access by road, are more spacious, offer a more attractive environment and are cheaper to develop (i.e. no expensive land reclamation is needed).

e.g. the UK government's estimate that 4.4 million new homes will be needed in the UK by 2016, 40% of which will be built on greenfield sites.

TIP Think of the disadvantages of greenfield sites — loss of countryside, increased car usage, longer commuter journeys etc. — and compare these with the advantages to developers and economic activities. You should formulate your own opinions on greenfield development before sitting your AS and A-level examinations.

G

greenhouse effect: increase in levels of carbon dioxide and other 'greenhouse' gases in the atmosphere, which are thought to be responsible for *global warming*.

▓ Carbon dioxide, methane and other 'greenhouse' gases are transparent to the sun's short-wave radiation, but absorb long-wave radiation from the Earth. With increasing levels of carbon dioxide etc. in the atmosphere, the input of energy (from the sun) exceeds the output (from the Earth). This imbalance is the so-called greenhouse effect and the probable cause of global warming.

green revolution: attempt to increase food production in LEDCs since the 1960s by introducing new *high-yielding varieties* (HYVs) of wheat and rice.

▓ The green revolution has increased food output, most noticeably in south and southeast Asia. However, its impact has been variable. For example, crops such as wheat and rice are largely unsuited to the climate and soil of some of the world's poorest countries in Africa. Compared to traditional varieties, some HYVs are susceptible to disease. HYVs require chemical fertilisers and irrigation water and thus favour better-off farmers on more productive land. As a result, the green revolution has often widened the gap between rich and poor.

▓ *TIP* The green revolution is not a single event. It has gone through a number of stages. Convey in your writing a sense that the green revolution is a complex change spread over a period of 30 years or so.

green tourism: alternative name for *ecotourism*.

groundwater: underground water stored in the pores and joints of *permeable rocks* or aquifers.

▓ Groundwater is the main source of base flow in streams and rivers. It reaches the surface through springs and seepage. The upper boundary of saturated rocks is known as the *water table*, and the steepness of the water table is the *hydraulic gradient*.

▓ *e.g.* The principal sources of groundwater in the UK are New Red Sandstone and chalk.

▓ *TIP* A common theme in question setting at AS and A-level is the sustainable use of groundwater. In the past, overpumping of groundwater from the chalk in southeast England led to a dramatic fall in the water table, causing some rivers to run dry. Sustainable use of groundwater means that the rate of abstraction is equal to the rate of rainfall recharge.

growing season: number of days in a year when temperatures and *precipitation* permit crop growth.

▓ In middle to high-latitude areas, the growing season is usually determined by temperature (thermal growing season). As a general rule, we assume that growth begins when the mean daily air temperature reaches 6 °C. In the tropics, where the thermal growing season often lasts all year round, soil moisture levels rather than temperature set limits to crop growth. This is the hydrological growing season. It depends not on the amount of precipitation, but on precipitation effectiveness.

- *e.g.* In England the thermal growing season varies from 322 days at sea level in Cornwall to 189 days at 315 m above sea level in the northern Pennines.
- *TIP* It is worth remembering that farmers can do far more to extend the hydrological growing season (through *irrigation*) than they can to extend the thermal growing season.

groyne: wood, metal or rock barrier, built at right angles to the shore and designed to intercept the *longshore drift* of sand and shingle.

- Groynes are simple *hard engineering* structures designed to build up beach material and keep it in situ. In coastal resorts, beach accumulation may be encouraged for amenity reasons. Well-developed beaches are also excellent absorbers of wave energy and play an important part in defending the coast against *erosion*.
- *e.g.* the groynefield at Hornsea in Holderness. The Holderness is one of Europe's most rapidly eroding coastlines.
- *TIP* You should consider the impact of groynes on the coastal sediment budget. While giving protection in their immediate vicinity, groynes may starve adjacent downdrift coastlines of beach sediment. The effect may be to accelerate erosion in these areas.

gully: small channel cut by *runoff* on incoherent rocks, on steep, unvegetated slopes.

- Gullies often occur at very high density, and because they form on steep slopes they show only limited branching.
- *e.g.* badland topography of South Dakota, developed on weak clays, shales and siltstones.

Hadley cell: large convective cell that dominates the atmospheric circulation in the tropics.

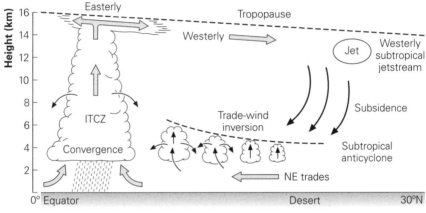

The Hadley cell in the northern hemisphere

■ There are two Hadley cells: one in each hemisphere. Intense heating of the surface in the equatorial zone leads to rising convectional currents, clouds, thunderstorms and permanent low pressure. This is the *inter-tropical convergence zone*. The air cools as it reaches the *tropopause* and is exported at this level polewards. Between 20 and 30 degrees north and south of the equator, the air begins to subside, forming permanent high pressure at the surface. The subsiding air warms dynamically and becomes extremely dry. The result is the formation of hot deserts such as the Sahara and Australian desert. A return flow of air from the permanent high pressure of the deserts to the permanent low around the equator (the trade winds) completes the convective cell.

■ *TIP* The climate at the Earth's surface is controlled by the atmospheric circulation. The Hadley cell explains many features of the climate of the tropics.

halosere: *plant succession* in a saline environment such as coastal *mudflats* and *salt marshes*.

■ Plant succession is accompanied by *accretion* (increasing the height of the surface) and by a gradual reduction in salinity and in the period of inundation on each high tide. Pioneer species include glasswort (Salicornia) and cord grass (Spartina).

hanging valley: tributary valley to a larger, overdeepened *glacial trough.*

■ Where the tributary valley (which may or may not have been glaciated) meets the main valley, it may 'hang' several hundred metres above the main valley floor. Hanging valleys are common features in former glaciated uplands.

■ *e.g.* the tributary valley to the Yosemite Valley (California), which is responsible for the spectacular Yosemite Falls.

hard engineering: responses to environmental problems such as coastal *erosion* and coastal flooding by building structures such as *sea walls, groynes, revetments* and flood barriers.

■ Hard engineering in coastal management is currently favoured only where there is a direct threat either to large centres of population or to important infrastructure. Such solutions are often expensive, environmentally damaging and unsustainable. Current thinking favours soft engineering solutions in coastal environments, including *beach nourishment* and *managed retreat.*

■ *e.g.* Thames barrier.

Harris–Ullman multiple-nuclei model: urban structure model that describes patterns of urban land use as a series of discrete nuclei.

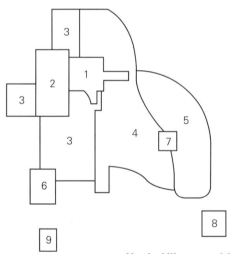

1 Central business district
2 Wholesale light manufacturing
3 Low-class residential
4 Medium-class residential
5 High-class residential
6 Heavy manufacturing
7 Outlying business district
8 Residential suburb
9 Industrial suburb

Harris–Ullman multiple-nuclei model

■ Unlike other structure models, the Harris–Ullman model gives little indication of the spatial patterning of urban land use. The idea that different land uses form discrete areas in the city is, however, useful.

HDI: see *human development index.*

head: unsorted *solifluction* deposit of stony material set in a stiff clay matrix.

■ Head is widespread in southern Britain, where it formed under *periglacial* conditions during the last *glacial.* The long axes of larger particles in head deposits are aligned downslope.

headland: promontory of resistant rock on an upland coast.

▓ Headlands are areas of concentrated wave energy. As a result, erosional landforms such as *caves*, sea *stacks* and arches are common on or around headlands.

▓ *e.g.* St Abb's Head, southeast Scotland, made of resistant andesitic and basaltic lavas.

heat island: higher average temperatures of urban areas compared with the surrounding countryside.

▓ The heat island effect is one of the most distinctive features of urban *micro-climates*. It is most apparent at night under calm conditions. Its causes are: the heat generated within urban areas (space heating, economic activities, transport); the heat-absorbent fabric of buildings (stored heat during the daytime is given out at night); and atmospheric pollution, which reduces heat loss.

helical flow: corkscrew-like flow of water in a meandering river channel.

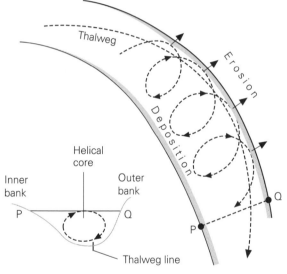

Helical flow in a meander

▓ Also known as helicoidal flow, helical flow comprises a current from the outer to the inner bank close to the river bed, and a return flow at or near the surface. Helical flow helps to explain sediment *accretion* on the inner bank of meandering channels, which forms *point bars*.

HEP: see *hydro-electric power*.

hierarchy: ranking of settlements at a global, national or regional scale according to some measure of their size and status.

▓ Settlement hierarchies are usually based on the number and range of services provided by each centre (see *central place theory*). A settlement hierarchy is an efficient way to provide the population of an area with the goods and services it needs.

high-tech industry: industries such as electronics and biotechnology that make advanced technology products and that spend at least 5% of their annual turnover on research, development and design.

■ High-tech industries have two strands: plants that develop new products, and plants that specialise in routine production of mature products (e.g. semi-conductors). The first group requires highly skilled scientists, engineers and technicians. They locate in *science parks* in environmentally attractive regions, close to universities and research institutions. The second rely on unskilled and semi-skilled labour. In MEDCs they have tended to locate in peripheral regions where government financial incentives are available. Increasingly, this type of high-tech plant is locating in LEDCs where labour costs are low.

■ *e.g.* In the UK, the largest cluster of high-tech industries involved in product development is Silicon Fen (Cambridge). The largest concentration of high-tech industries involved in routine production in the UK is Silicon Glen (central Scotland).

■ *TIP* Many students quote high-tech industries as examples of *footloose industries.* In the sense that they are little affected in their choice of location by traditional location factors, this is true. However, it is a misconception to believe that high-tech industries can locate anywhere. High-tech industries have specific locational requirements, which is why they often show a strong tendency to cluster.

high-yielding varieties: dwarf varieties of rice and wheat bred in the 1960s, which gave improved yields and were the basis of the *green revolution.*

■ Although high-yielding varieties of rice and wheat increased food production in many LEDCs, they were successful only when used in conjunction with *agro-chemicals* (fertilisers, pesticides) and *irrigation.*

hinterland: see *trade area.*

Hjulström curve: model that shows the relationship between flow velocity and the transport of particles of varying size in a stream or river.

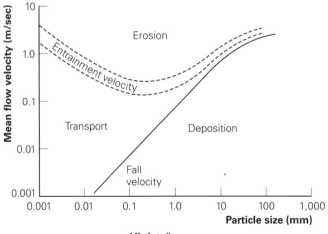

Hjulström curve

▓ The model has two curves: the upper one shows the critical erosion velocity needed to transport particles; and the lower one shows the fall velocity needed for deposition. The critical erosion velocity is high for both coarse particles and fine particles. Sand-sized particles are entrained at relatively low velocities. Deposition of coarse particles occurs at high velocities, but deposition of fine particles occurs only at very low velocities. The surprising feature of the model is the high velocities needed to transport fine particles. This is because these particles are bonded by electrical attraction and are highly coherent.

▓ *TIP* Consider the implications of the model for the transport of a river's load at high discharge. Large particles will move only while velocity remains high, which may be for just an hour or two. Fine particles will also need similar high velocities to move, but because they settle out at very low velocities, once entrained they will be transported for long distances.

honeypot: highly popular location for visitors in a conservation area such as a *National Park*.

▓ Honeypots are usually easily accessible and have attractions for mass tourism, such as visitor centres, shops, cafés, parking areas and trails. Planners in recreational areas often promote honeypot sites. This strategy helps to protect more environmentally sensitive sites, and preserves most of the conservation area for quiet, sustainable recreation.

▓ *e.g.* Coniston in the Lake District National Park.

horizontal organisation: manufacturing activity with a geographically dispersed production chain.

▓ Parts and components manufacture is subcontracted to many firms, and these items are eventually brought together for final assembly. A horizontal organisation has a number of advantages (e.g. parts suppliers can specialise in a single product and achieve *economies of scale*; smaller firms are more flexible and can respond rapidly to changing demand) (see *flexible production*).

▓ *e.g.* the motor vehicle industry, where parts manufacture is subcontracted to hundreds of different firms.

▓ *TIP* You should consider the advantages of horizontal organisation alongside the alternative production strategy — *vertical integration*.

horticulture: see *market gardening*.

hot spot: area of intense volcanic activity located where *magma* from a rising mantle plume reaches the Earth's surface.

▓ *e.g.* the Big Island of Hawaii, where Mauna Loa and Kilauea are two of the world's most active *volcanoes*.

▓ *TIP* Hot spots are the exception to the general rule that volcanic activity is confined to plate boundaries.

Hoyt's urban sector model: classic urban structure model in which land use is organised as a series of sectors radiating from the city centre.

▓ The Hoyt model suggests that cities expand outwards along radial roads, rivers, canals, railways, etc. which give good accessibility. A sectoral arrangement also assists segregation of different socio-economic and ethnic groups, and concentrates *externalities* such as pollution in particular areas.

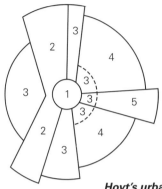

1 Central business district
2 Wholesale light manufacturing
3 Low-class residential
4 Medium-class residential
5 High-class residential

Hoyt's urban sector model

▨ *TIP* Don't expect to a find a city that corresponds exactly with the Hoyt model. The model shows how some types of urban land use develop a sectoral pattern. You can probably identify at least one or two sectors in most cities.

Huff's interaction model: a type of interaction or *gravity model* that shows the probability of shoppers purchasing goods and services in particular settlements in a region.

▨ The Huff model assumes that the 'pull' of a shopping centre is proportional to its attractiveness (e.g. size, number/range/quality of shops) and inversely proportional to its accessibility (e.g. distance, travelling time, cost of travel). Unlike the gravity model, the Huff model takes account of competition from other centres. The probability of a trip from area i to centre 1 (S_1), in a region with three shopping centres (S_1, S_2, S_3), is given in the formula below.

$$P_{il} = \frac{\dfrac{S_1}{D_{i1}}}{\dfrac{S_1}{D_{i1}} + \dfrac{S_2}{D_{i2}} + \dfrac{S_3}{D_{i3}}}$$

where P_{il} = probability of trip from area i to centre 1
S = the attractiveness of the centre
D = distance/accessibility from area i to a centre

human development index (HDI): UN-devised measure of human well-being based on both social and economic criteria.

▨ The human development index (HDI) is applied at a national scale. It combines data on *mortality*, adult literacy, schooling and the purchasing power of incomes. It ranges from 0 (least developed) to 1 (most developed). The HDI is a more sensitive measure of human well-being than GNP per capita because it takes into account social as well as economic criteria.

▨ *e.g.* In 1998 the HDI for the world's richest (OEDC) countries averaged 0.900, compared to an average of 0.430 for the least developed countries.

humidity: amount of water vapour present in the air.

There are two measures of humidity: absolute humidity and relative humidity. Absolute humidity is the actual amount of moisture (in grams m^{-3}) in the air. Relative humidity (as a percentage) is the amount of moisture in the air compared to the amount needed to saturate the air. Absolute humidity is determined by temperature: warm air can hold far more moisture than cold air.

hummocky moraine: conical-shaped mounds of *boulder clay* that are often highly concentrated within a small area.

Hummocky moraines are interpreted as melt-out deposits. Most were formed by the last ice advance in the Loch Lomond inter-stadial (11,000–10,000 years BP) and mark the terminal position reached by valley *glaciers*.

e.g. the hummocky moraines in Glen Torridon, which are the most extensive in the British Isles.

humus: partly decomposed organic material in the soil.

Humus is an important source of plant nutrients and combines with clays to form the colloidal complex in the soil. Soils rich in humus also have good water-retaining qualities. There are two main types of humus: mull humus, produced by many broad-leaved trees (e.g. oak), is mildly acidic, easily decomposed and base-rich; mor humus, produced by conifer trees, moorland and heathland vegetation, is acidic, slow to decompose and nutrient-deficient. Moder is a type of humus of intermediate status.

hurricane: powerful tropical storm associated with violent winds, torrential rain and widespread flooding.

Hurricanes are also known as tropical cyclones in south Asia and typhoons in east and southeast Asia. They form in tropical oceans where surface waters reach a temperature of at least 27°C. They are powered by the latent heat derived from the *evaporation* of water from the oceans. Hurricanes are most damaging in coastal areas, where strong winds and low pressure cause storm surges. Deprived of their power source, hurricanes quickly decay as they move inland.

e.g. Hurricane Opal, which devastated the Gulf states of the USA in 1995, causing 28 deaths. In the wake of the storm, 104 official disaster areas were declared by the government in Florida, Georgia, Alabama and South Carolina.

hydration: *weathering* process that involves the absorption of water by minerals, causing swelling that leads to rock distintegration.

hydraulic geometry: changes that occur in the width, depth, gradient and efficiency (velocity) of river channels with increasing discharge.

Hydraulic geometry explains how a river's channel adjusts to increasing *bankfull* discharge both downstream and at a station.

e.g. A study along a 5 km stretch of Eglingham Burn (a tributary of the River Aln in Northumberland) showed a 285% increase in bankfull discharge, with a 60% increase in depth, a 35% increase in velocity and a 30% increase in width.

TIP The response of the river channel to increasing discharge will depend on local circumstances. If you are writing about hydraulic geometry in an examination, make reference to local conditions (e.g. well-vegetated banks, solid rock in the channel) that might help to explain the changes you describe.

hydraulic gradient: surface slope of the *water table* along which groundwater flows.

hydraulic radius (*r*): measurement of the efficiency of the cross-sectional shape of a river channel.

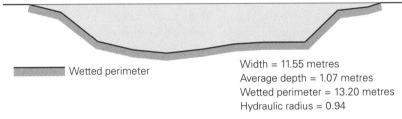

Wetted perimeter

Width = 11.55 metres
Average depth = 1.07 metres
Wetted perimeter = 13.20 metres
Hydraulic radius = 0.94

Bankfull channel cross-section: Eglingham Burn, Northumberland

The hydraulic radius is the ratio of a channel's cross-sectional area to its *wetted perimeter*. The higher the value of *r*, the more efficient the flow. This is because less energy is lost to friction between the water and the channel bed and banks. The most efficient channel shape for transporting water is semi-circular.

TIP Channel gradients decrease downstream (see *graded profile*), yet velocity increases. This relationship seems to go against common sense and often confuses students. However, you must understand that any decrease in gradient is more than compensated by the increased efficiency of the channel (as measured by *r*).

hydro-electric power (HEP): generation of electricity by the force of water.

HEP may be generated by large, fast-flowing rivers or by the fall of water (e.g. at a dam or in areas of strong relief). HEP is a non-polluting *renewable* source of energy. However, it does have environmental costs (e.g. flooding valleys) and ultimately all reservoirs silt up.

e.g. Glen Canyon Dam on the River Colorado, which supplies electricity to Arizona but has flooded huge areas of canyon lands (Lake Powell). The dam has also regulated the flow of the Colorado River. The river no longer floods and this has had adverse effects on the ecology of the Grand Canyon.

hydrograph: discharge curve for a stream or river.

Hydrographs may record a single storm (as in the diagram) or river flow on a daily, monthly or annual basis. Average monthly and average annual flows are known as the *river's regime*. Storm (or flood) hydrographs plot hourly discharge (often in $m^3 \ sec^{-1}$) and hourly *precipitation*. The most important features of storm hydrographs are *lag time* and peak discharge. The shape of the discharge curve reflects both fixed drainage basin characteristics (e.g. geology, slopes, drainage density, land use) and variable characteristics (e.g. precipitation amount, precipitation intensity, soil moisture conditions, *evapotranspiration*, snow cover). Rivers with high peak discharges and short lag time (so-called flashy rivers) are most liable to flood.

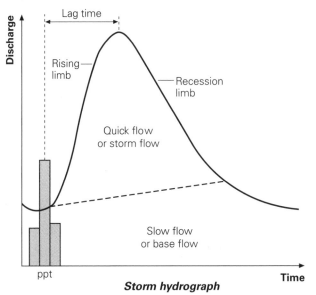

Storm hydrograph

hydrological cycle: alternative name for the *water cycle*.

hydrolysis: *weathering* process that involves a chemical reaction between rock minerals and water.

■ Hydrogen and hydroxyl from the dissociation of water cause the breakdown of silicate minerals in *igneous rocks*.

■ *e.g.* Feldspar, an important constituent of granite, is susceptible to weathering by hydrolysis. The outcome of weathering is the formation of a white clay mineral known as kaolinite (or china clay).

■ *TIP* The weathering processes on granite are often inaccurately understood. Apart from hydrolysis you should ignore all other *chemical weathering* processes (e.g. *solution, oxidation, hydration*) when writing about the weathering of granite.

hydrosere: *plant succession* in a freshwater environment.

■ Succession is accompanied by a gradual drying-out of the environment through siltation and the accumulation of plant remains. *Pioneer communities* include aquatic plants such as reeds, rushes, flag iris and water crowfoot.

■ *e.g.* plant succession around a pond or lakeshore.

ice age: popular term for a *glacial*.

ice cap: alternative name for an *ice sheet*.

icefield: large body of ice usually occupying a plateau-like area in high latitudes or high mountains.

■ Tongues of faster-moving ice within an icefield spill over the edge of the ice-covered plateau to form outlet *glaciers*.

■ *e.g.* the Columbia icefield in the Canadian Rockies.

ice lens: lens-shaped bodies of ground ice that develop below and parallel to the surface in *periglacial environments*.

■ Ice lenses are a form of segregated ice that develops by the migration of water through the *regolith*. They are most commonly developed in fine, silty regolith.

ice sheet: very large, stable *glacier* that can survive prolonged periods of warming (e.g. *inter-glacials*).

■ Ice sheets are not constrained in their flow by the nature of the underlying topography.

■ *e.g.* Antarctic ice sheet.

■ *TIP* Ice sheets, similar to those in Antarctica and Greenland, covered most of North America and northern Europe during the last *glacial*. They (rather than valley glaciers) were responsible for major erosional and depositional landforms such as *glacial troughs* and *drumlins*.

ice stream: narrow zone of fast-flowing ice within *ice sheets*.

■ Ice streams often feed outlet *glaciers* that flow from plateau-like *icefields* and ice sheets to lower ground.

■ *e.g.* During the last glacial, the Cairngorm Plateau was submerged by an icefield. Ice on the plateau was frozen to the underlying bedrock and incapable of much *erosion*. Over the valleys, where the ice was thicker, fast-moving ice streams developed, further eroding the valleys and creating huge *glacial troughs* such as Glen Derry.

ice wedge: downward-tapering body of ground ice found in *periglacial environments*.

■ Ice wedges have a polygonal planform and give rise to *patterned ground*. Ice wedges form by frost cracking, which is the result of extreme cold and contraction of the ground (rather like mud drying out in a puddle).

igneous intrusion: landform that originates from the emplacement of *magma* within the Earth's crust.

■ There are major and minor igneous intrusions. *Batholiths* are major igneous intrusions. They may consist of hundreds of cubic kilometres of coarse igneous rock such as granite and gabbro. Minor igneous intrusions occur on a much smaller scale and include *sills* and *dykes*.

■ *e.g.* a major igneous intrusion: the granite batholith that forms the Mourne Mountains in Northern Ireland; a minor igneous intrusion: the Great Whin Sill in the northern Pennines.

igneous rock: type of rock derived from *magma*.

■ Igneous rocks may be intrusive or extrusive; crystalline or non-crystalline. Intrusive igneous rocks comprise minerals that crystallised from magma that cooled below the surface. Extrusive igneous rocks formed from material erupted at the surface by *volcanoes* and volcanic fissures. These rocks comprise either solidified lava (crystalline) or accumulations of ash and pyroclasts (non-crystalline).

■ *e.g.* intrusive igneous rocks: granite, gabbro, dolerite; extrusive igneous rocks: *basalt*, rhyolite (crystalline); tuff (non-crystalline).

■ *TIP* Both intrusive and extrusive igneous rocks are resistant to *erosion* and consequently produce a number of striking landforms, including *batholiths*, *bosses*, *lava plateaux*, *dykes* and *sills*.

illuviation: deposition or washing-in of minerals, nutrients and *humus* from a surface to a sub-surface soil horizon.

■ Illuviation involves the downwashing of both solid particles and those in solution (*leaching*).

■ *e.g.* The B horizon in podzolised soils is an illuviated horizon.

■ *TIP* Be sure to distinguish accurately the processes of *eluviation*, *cheluviation* and illuviation.

immigration: movement of people into a country, region or locality which involves a permanent change of residence.

■ Immigration (like *emigration*) is a response to *push–pull factors*. These factors may be economic (e.g employment), social (e.g. schools, health care), political (e.g. persecution for beliefs), environmental (e.g. natural disasters), etc.

■ *e.g.* the movement of Kosovan refugees to the UK in 1999 following the war between Serbia and NATO.

■ *TIP* Immigration is simply an alternative term for in-migration. If you find it difficult to remember the terms 'immigration' and 'emigration', use in-migration and out-migration instead.

import substitution: promotion and development of industries within a country aimed at reducing manufacturing imports.

■ Import substitution is part of a strategy for industrial development that includes four stages: (1) industries based on local advantages (materials, skills, cheap labour); (2) import substitution industries; (3) export-oriented industries; (4) overseas investment.

■ *e.g.* Botswana in the 1990s developed a number of import substitution industries, including the assembly of motor vehicles based on imported parts.

independent retailer: small retailer, independently owned and with just one or a few outlets.

■ Independent retailers have been severely hit by the expansion of *multiple retailers* in the last 30 years. Small independent food stores have found it particularly hard to compete with supermarket giants such as Tesco, Sainsbury's and Asda.

industrial estate: modern industrial area with purpose-built units and good road access, often located on the edge of town.

■ *e.g.* Team Valley, Gateshead.

industrial inertia: survival of a manufacturing industry or manufacturing firm in an area, even though the *initial advantages* of the location no longer apply.

■ Industrial inertia largely results from the immobility of fixed capital (e.g. plant and machinery).

■ *e.g.* the survival of iron and steel making at Scunthorpe, Lincolnshire. The plant is located inland and sourcing of materials is more expensive than a location at tidewater (see *tidewater industry*).

■ *TIP* Industrial inertia is an ambiguous concept. Although the initial advantages of location (e.g. raw materials) may no longer apply, there may be sound economic reasons (*acquired advantages*) for an industry to remain where it first started (e.g. skilled labour, *external economies*).

industrialisation: rapid growth of manufacturing industry in a country or region.

■ Industrialisation produces a sectoral shift, in terms of employment and gross domestic product, in favour of manufacturing industry. It also leads to rural–urban *migration* and *urbanisation*. The process of industrialisation first took place in the UK in the nineteenth century.

■ *e.g.* Today's industrialising countries are LEDCs such as China, India, Thailand and Brazil.

infant mortality: number of deaths of infants under one year old per 1,000 live births.

■ Infant mortality is a very sensitive indicator of human well-being, including standards of housing, diet, health and hygiene. Thus infant mortality is much higher in LEDCs than in MEDCs.

■ *e.g.* In 1997 global infant mortality rates ranged from 5 per 1,000 in Denmark to 147 per 1,000 in Afghanistan.

■ *TIP* Infant mortality rates have a major effect on average life expectancy. The average life expectancy at birth in Afghanistan is just 47 years. But such a low figure is largely explained by the county's high infant mortality rate. For children surviving their first year, average life expectancy in Afghanistan is more than 60 years.

infiltration capacity: maximum rate at which water, under the pull of gravity, soaks into the soil.

■ Infiltration capacity depends primarily on the amount of water already in the soil and the size of pores or air spaces between soil particles. If the intensity of rainfall exceeds the soil's infiltration capacity, water should run off the surface as *overland flow*. Overland flow also occurs when the soil is saturated.

■ *e.g.* Coarse, sandy soils have large infiltration capacities; clayey soils have low capacities.

informal sector: economic activities in cities in LEDCs that are unregulated, in which workers are self-employed non-wage earners and are not protected by labour codes.

■ Depending on the precise definition used, up to half of all workers in many cities in LEDCs may be employed in the informal sector.

■ *e.g.* petty service activities such as street hawking, garbage pickers and shoe shiners.

■ *TIP* Don't underestimate the importance of the informal sector in LEDCs. The formal economic sector (regular waged employment) is unable to satisfy the demand for employment. The informal sector, being *labour-intensive* and easy to access, 'soaks up' millions of workers who would otherwise be unemployed.

infrastructure: fixed capital investment in transport networks, utility grids, housing, hospitals, schools etc. essential to the functioning of the economy and society.

■ The absence of an effective infrastructure in many LEDCs is a major obstacle to economic and social development.

initial advantages: reasons why an economic activity first located in a place.

■ In the nineteenth century, prohibitive transport costs often constrained industry to locate close to materials, energy sources and markets.

■ *e.g.* The iron-making industry in the UK in the nineteenth century located on coalfields and orefields.

■ *TIP* Remember that changing technology often means that sites chosen for their initial advantages eventually become obsolete. However, an industry may remain on site because of (a) *industrial inertia* or (b) *acquired advantages*.

inner city: zone of mixed land use (mainly housing and industry) within 1 or 2 km of the central business district.

■ Inner cities have become synonymous with urban decay in MEDCs. Despite urban redevelopment (and in some areas *gentrification*), much of the inner city remains an area of poor-quality housing with populations suffering *social exclusion* and multiple deprivation (poor schools and other services, few job opportunities, high levels of crime, high unemployment, pollution etc.).

■ *e.g.* Well-known inner city areas in British cities include Toxteth (Liverpool), Moss Side (Manchester), Sparkbrook (Birmingham), Benwell (Newcastle upon Tyne) and St Paul's (Bristol).

■ *TIP* Students commonly mistake the *central business district* (CBD) for part of the inner city. The CBD is a quite separate area and should not be considered in examination questions focusing on the inner city.

inselberg: isolated, steep-sided rocky monolith.

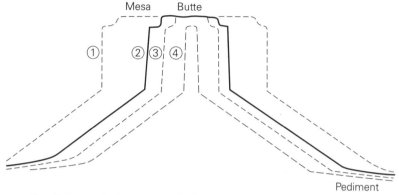

Parallel retreat of a structural plateau, resulting in the formation of inselbergs (mesas and buttes)

■ Inselbergs include mesas, buttes, *bornhardts* and *exfoliation domes*. Inselbergs may result from the *parallel retreat* of slopes in areas where sedimentary rocks are horizontally bedded (e.g. mesas and buttes), or from sub-surface *chemical weathering* and exhumation of unweathered rock masses (e.g born-hardts).

■ *e.g.* Merrick Butte, Monument Valley, Arizona — a sandstone monolith formed by river incision into a structural plateau and parallel retreat of slopes.

insolation: incoming solar radiation.

■ Most insolation is short-wave radiation concentrated in the visible band of the spectrum. Because of reflection, absorption and scattering, only 45% of insolation reaches the Earth's surface. Although the amount of radiation received at the top of the atmosphere is constant for all parts of the globe, the Earth's curvature means that the intensity of insolation is much higher in the tropics than in middle-latitude and polar regions. The difference in solar radiation receipt between the tropics and the poles results in a poleward transport of energy. This energy transport powers the atmosphere's general circulation (see *global energy budget*).

instability: atmospheric condition when a parcel of air is warmer than its surroundings and, if displaced, rises freely through the atmosphere.

■ Instability develops when an air parcel in contact with the ground is heated by either convection or advection (see *convectional precipitation* and *fog*). Rising, unstable air undergoes *adiabatic cooling* and condenses to form *cumuliform clouds*, which may produce showers or thunderstorms. Absolute instability is when both dry and saturated air parcels are unstable. Conditional instability is when dry air is stable and saturated air is unstable.

■ *e.g.* The presence of cumulus clouds is an indication of atmospheric instability.

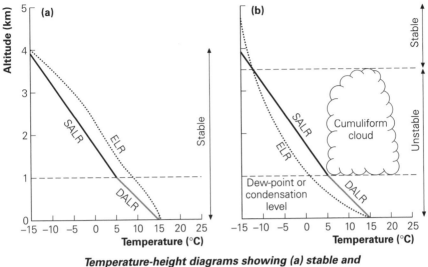

Temperature-height diagrams showing (a) stable and (b) unstable atmospheric conditions

■ **TIP** The concepts of *stability* and instability often cause problems at AS and A-level. It helps to remember that they refer to the temperature of air parcels relative to the background temperature of the atmosphere.

intensive agriculture: type of agriculture where high inputs of labour or capital (e.g. fertiliser) per hectare give high outputs (yields) per hectare.

■ Intensive agriculture most often occurs when population pressure is high and when farms are small. Subsistence farmers have to maximise yields in order to produce sufficient food to survive; commercial farmers maximise yields to achieve the profits needed to remain in business.

■ *e.g.* intensive polyculture in east Asia, based on rice, vegetables and silk worms; *market gardening* in the Westland region of the Netherlands.

interception: *precipitation* that is trapped or stored temporarily on the surfaces of plant leaves, stems, branches, etc.

■ The amount of interception varies according to the density of vegetation cover, season and the intensity of precipitation. Interception slows the movement of water to stream and river channels, and increases moisture loss through *evaporation*.

interdependence: interrelationship between MEDCs and LEDCs through trade, *foreign direct investment, foreign aid* and *migration*.

■ The relationship between MEDCs and LEDCs is often seen as one-sided, placing LEDCs in a position of dependency.

■ *e.g.* In 1994 the value of all exports from MEDCs to LEDCs was $735 billion; exports worth just $650 billion flowed in the opposite direction.

■ **TIP** When revising this topic for examination, you should be aware of both the advantages and disadvantages of interdependence for MEDCs and LEDCs, and be prepared to evaluate them in discussion.

inter-glacial: warm climatic interlude between *glacials* or ice ages, lasting for approximately 10,000 years.

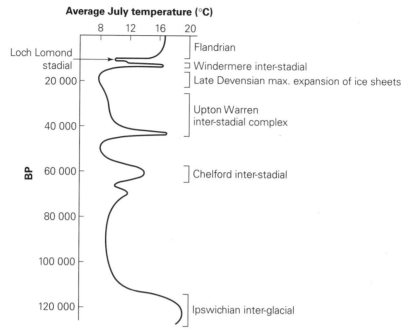

Average July temperature (°C)

Variations in average Devensian July temperatures in lowland areas of southern and central British Isles

- Inter-glacials see the retreat of *ice sheets* from northern Europe and North America, the colonisation of plants and animals in previously glaciated areas and rising sea levels that flood continental shelf areas.
- *e.g.* The Earth is currently in an inter-glacial — the Holocene. The Holocene has lasted for around 10,000 years. The whole of civilisation and recorded history has occurred during the current inter-glacial.
- *TIP* It is easy to confuse inter-glacials and *inter-stadials*. An inter-stadial is a much shorter period of climatic amelioration (e.g. the Windermere inter-stadial lasting from around 13,000 years BP to 11,000 years BP).

interlocking spurs: see *V-shaped valley*.

intermediate technology: simple low-cost technology that is appropriate to the skills and needs of communities in LEDCs.

- Intermediate technology provides simple, practical and sustainable solutions to the problems of poor communities in LEDCs. Through the use of intermediate technology, these communities can help themselves and develop their traditional skills.
- *e.g.* the introduction in Darfur, western Sudan, of a donkey-drawn plough. This helped farmers increase the cultivated area and compensated for losses caused by drought and *desertification*.

internal economies of scale: savings in unit costs that arise from large-scale production.

▨ Three factors explain the savings that arise from large-scale production: (a) fixed costs, such as research and development, and local taxes, can be spread across a greater number of units produced; (b) increased opportunities for the specialisation of labour; and (c) discounts available for purchasing materials in bulk.

▨ *e.g.* the modern iron and steel industry, where scale economies demand an output of at least 3 or 4 million tonnes of steel a year per plant.

▨ *TIP* Internal economies of scale derive from within a plant; *external economies of scale* derive from linkages to other firms and infrastructure outside the plant. The term 'economies of scale' covers both internal and external economies.

inter-quartile range: measure of dispersion around the median value in a data set (see *measures of central tendency*).

▨ Values in a data set are ranked in order of size and divided into four equal groups or quartiles. The boundary between the first and second quartiles is known as the upper quartile, while the boundary between the third and fourth quartiles is the lower quartile. The difference between the upper and lower quartiles is the inter-quartile range.

▨ *e.g.* upper quartile = 56; lower quartile = 22. The inter-quartile range is 56 − 22 = 34.

▨ *TIP* Like other measures of dispersion (e.g. standard deviation), the inter-quartile range tells us how values are distributed around a single central value, in this case the median. It is most useful where data have a *skewed frequency distribution*.

inter-stadial: relatively short-lived warmer period during a *glacial* or ice age.

▨ *e.g.* the Windermere inter-stadial, which lasted from 13,000 to 11,000 years BP.

inter-tidal area: inshore area between the mean high water mark and the mean low water mark.

▨ The extent of the inter-tidal area depends on the tidal range and the gradient of the inshore area. Extensive inter-tidal areas are often associated with tidal landforms such as *mudflats* and *salt marshes*. Beaches such as *spits, tombolos* and *barrier beach islands* are found where inter-tidal areas are relatively narrow.

▨ *e.g.* the inter-tidal area between the Northumberland mainland and Lindisfarne, which at low tide forms extensive sandflats and mudflats.

inter-tropical convergence zone (ITCZ): area of permanent low pressure around the equator which forms the rising limb of the *Hadley cells*.

▨ Intense *insolation* and the convergence of the trade winds on the equator cause a belt of *instability* and rising air. The ITCZ is marked by towering cumulo-nimbus clouds and convective storms. The ITCZ shifts north of the equator between March and June, following the overhead sun. A similar movement of the ITCZ into the southern hemisphere occurs between September and

December. The movement of the ITCZ is responsible for wet and dry seasons in most of the tropics.

intrazonal soil: mature soil that owes its main features to the influence of a non-climatic factor such as parent material.

■ Intrazonal soils belong to the *zonal soil* classification which assumes that climate determines the characteristics of most mature soils. The intrazonal soil class covers those mature soils that are not climatically determined.

■ *e.g.* podzolic soils that have developed as a response to a sandy parent material in the Breckland in Norfolk.

■ *TIP* The zonal soil classification assumes that climate is the dominant soil-forming factor. Intrazonal soils are ones where a non-climatic soil-forming factor dominates.

inverted relief: type of topography where anticlinal structures (see *folding*) have eroded more rapidly than synclinal structures (see *syncline*) to form lower ground.

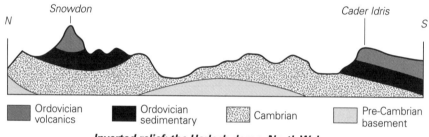

Inverted relief: the Harlech dome, North Wales

■ *Folding* produces the greatest stresses along anticlinal axes where *joint* widening occurs. These joints become the sites of concentrated *weathering* and *erosion*. Thus the anticlines that initially formed the hills become the lowlands after prolonged erosion.

■ *e.g.* The Vale of Pewsey to the north of Salisbury Plain is a lowland area formed along the axis of an anticline.

inward investment: see *foreign direct investment*.

iron pan: thin iron-cemented layer that occurs in the B horizon in *podzol* soils.

■ Iron pans develop from iron sesquioxides transferred by *leaching* from the upper horizons of podzolic soils, to accumulate in the B horizon. The presence of an iron pan may impede soil drainage and lead to the formation of a gley soil.

irrigation: artificial watering of crops.

■ Irrigation is a modification of the hydrological environment to allow crop growth or improve yields. Cultivation in many dryland environments (e.g. Nile Valley) is only possible with irrigation. In the UK, irrigation of some crops occurs in summer to combat soil drought. Irrigation water may be delivered to crops by canals, sprinklers and drip feeds. Excessive use of irrigation water in some dryland areas has caused *salinisation* and land abandonment (e.g. Indus Valley in Pakistan).

■ *e.g.* the cultivation of fruit and vegetables in California's San Joaquin Valley, using irrigation water from the Sierra Nevada and Colorado River.

island arc: chain of volcanic islands formed along a *subduction zone* between two oceanic plates.

■ Melt from the subducted plate reaches the sea bed, where it forms an arc of submarine *volcanoes*. Eruptions continue until the volcanoes rise above sea level and form a chain of islands.

■ *e.g.* the Kuril Islands formed along the subduction zone between the Pacific and Eurasian plates.

isobar: isoline on a weather chart or climate map that joins places of equal pressure.

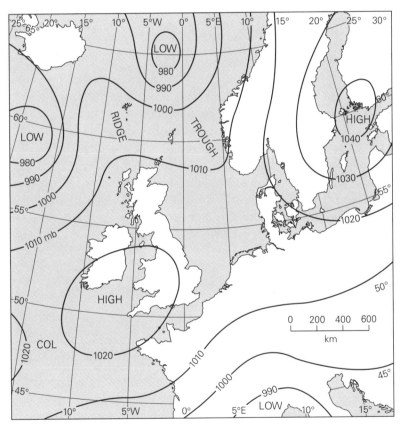

Some common patterns of sea-level isobars

■ Because altitude has a major effect on pressure, isobars are usually standardised to sea level. Pressure is measured in millibars (mb) and isobars are drawn at 4 mb intervals. Many weather features have distinctive isobaric patterns. Isobars that are packed together describe a steep *pressure gradient* and indicate strong winds. Widely spaced isobars show a slack pressure gradient and areas of light winds.

TIP When interpreting weather charts, an accurate understanding of the behaviour of winds in relation to isobars is essential. Winds blow at a slight angle to isobars, slanting inwards towards areas of low pressure, and outwards towards areas of high pressure. In the northern hemisphere, winds circulate clockwise around *anticyclones*, and anticlockwise around *depressions*.

isochrone: isoline that shows journey times to or from a place.

Journey times are a more accurate measure of the deterrence to travel than physical distance. The 1 hour isochrone is a reasonable estimate of a city's commuter hinterland.

TIP When discussing the frictional effect of distance on interaction, it is important to consider all three distance measures: physical distance (kilometres), journey time and financial cost.

isopleth map: statistical map that shows the distribution of a variable as a series of isopleths (or isolines).

Isopleth maps are the most appropriate technique to represent the distribution of phenomena which vary continuously over space (e.g. relief, temperature, *precipitation*, land value). They are less effective with variables such as population and factories that have specific point locations.

e.g. a weather chart with pressure represented as *isobars*.

isostacy: see *glacio-isostacy*.

isotropic surface: simplifying assumption made in many economic models that the Earth's surface is uniform and undifferentiated.

An isotropic surface is geographically the same everywhere: relief, soils, climate, population distribution, accessibility and so on are uniform. By making such a simplifying assumption, it is possible to isolate the influence of a single factor, such as distance, on spatial patterns.

e.g. *Central place theory* assumes an isotropic surface. This allows the theory to predict an idealised settlement pattern that minimises the distances travelled by consumers to buy the goods and services they need.

TIP The simplifying assumption of isotropism means that models such as central place theory bear little resemblance to reality. However, remember that the purpose of such models is not to explain reality. Their idealised outcomes tell us how the world should be organised given an isotropic surface and specific objectives (e.g. to minimise travel costs).

ITCZ: see *inter-tropical convergence zone*.

jet stream: high-velocity belt of fast-moving air that encircles the globe at the level of the *tropopause* in middle and high latitudes.

▨ The jet stream is the main feature of the atmosphere's circulation in middle and high latitudes. It flows from west to east in three to five meandering waves (Rossby waves). The position and amplitude of these waves has a direct influence on the formation of *depressions* and *anticyclones* and spells of weather lasting several weeks. Extreme weather conditions (drought, hot summers, cold winters) associated with high pressure occur when the jet stream has four or five waves. Unsettled conditions, with a strong westerly flow, occur when there are just three or four low-amplitude waves.

JIT: see *just-in-time*.

joint: fracture in a rock that has not caused displacement on either side.

▨ Joints develop from stresses and earth movements. They are lines of weakness in rocks that allow the ingress of water and air. As a result, they are sites of concentrated *weathering*. Shrinkage joints form in sedimentary rocks as the drying rock becomes more compact. *Igneous rocks* have both vertical and horizontal joints. Vertical joints develop perpendicular to the surface and are caused by contraction cooling. Horizontal joints develop parallel to the surface and result from unloading and *pressure release*.

▨ *e.g.* hexagonal columnar jointing in *basalt* lava at the Giant's Causeway, Northern Ireland.

jökulhlaup: catastrophic flood suddenly released by a *glacier*.

▨ Water may be released from glacier cavities and sub-glacial lakes. The most powerful jökulhlaups occur when a dam impounding a sub-glacial lake bursts.

▨ *e.g.* A jökulhlaup occurred in Iceland in 1996 when the Loki *volcano* erupted beneath the Vatnajökull icefield. It formed a sub-glacial lake of over $3\,km^3$ of meltwater. Peak discharge was around 45,000 cumecs.

just-in-time (JIT): supply of parts by subcontractors to an assembly line as they are needed.

▨ JIT systems are part of lean production in modern manufacturing. They have considerable economic advantages for firms buying in components and responsible for final assembly. In particular, these firms do not have the cost of keeping extensive stocks of components on site. However, the quality of components must be high, with zero defects. JIT should lead to the geographical clustering of parts suppliers and assemblers.

■ *e.g.* the clustering of Japanese car assembly plants and parts suppliers in the Tokyo region of Japan, which allows true JIT systems to operate.

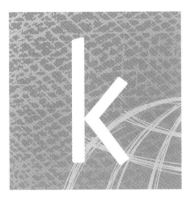

kame: mound of sediment formed initially by deposition in a cavity in a *glacier*, followed by slumping as the ice melted (see *landslide*).

Kames are small-scale features formed from stratified glacio-fluvial sands and gravels.

kame terrace: terrace of *glacio-fluvial deposits* formed along the side of a glacial valley.

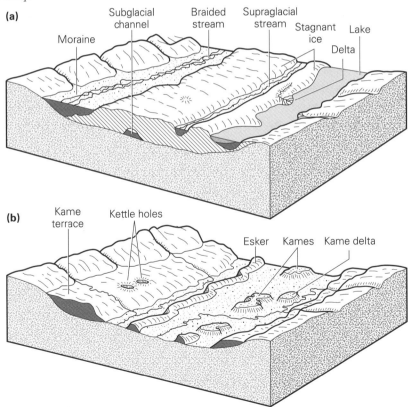

Development of glacio-fluvial landforms and deposits including kames and kame terraces: (a) late stage of deglaciation with extensive areas of stagnant ice and abundant meltwater; (b) after deglaciation

Kame terraces are formed by the accumulation of sediment in shallow lakes between the ice margin and the edge of the valley. When the supporting ice walls melted, the sediments collapsed, leaving a flat-topped embankment running along the valley side.

karst: Carboniferous limestone scenery.

Karst scenery consists of landforms developed by the solution of limestone (e.g. *dolines, swallow holes, caves,* caverns). There are two types of tropical karst scenery: cockpit karst with cone-shaped hills interspersed with deep dolines; and tower karst dominated by isolated limestone monoliths (mogotes).

e.g. The classic karst landscapes in the British Isles are in the Burren (County Clare) and the Yorkshire Dales. Cockpit karst is found in Jamaica; tower karst in eastern China.

TIP When analysing karst landscapes in the British Isles, you should distinguish between those landforms that develop from the *solution* (*carbonation*) of limestone, and those, such as limestone pavements, *screes* and *dry valleys,* that formed under glacial and *periglacial* conditions (glacio-karst).

katabatic wind: downslope flow of cold air at night into valleys.

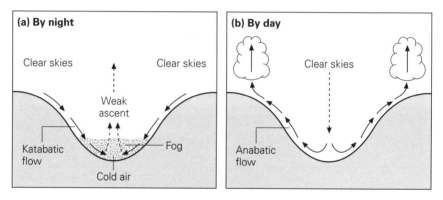

Katabatic and anabatic airflows

At night, air in contact with valley slopes cools more rapidly (by radiative cooling) than air above the valley at the same height. The colder, denser air drains downslope, displacing the warmer air. Cold air accumulating in the valley will create a *temperature inversion* and may form an inversion fog or valley fog (see *fog*).

TIP Katabatic and anabatic flows are local winds caused by the effect of relief on local energy budgets (also see *anabatic wind*). Katabatic flows are downslope; anabatic flows are upslope.

kettlehole: surface depression in glacial deposits, usually filled with water, caused by the melting of buried ice and resulting subsidence.

knickpoint: localised steepening of a river's long profile caused by *rejuvenation*.

A fall in *base level* produces renewed downcutting by a river and the development of a new *graded profile*. This new profile starts near the river's mouth and slowly migrates upstream. The point where the new profile intersects the old one is known as a knickpoint. It may be marked by rapids or waterfalls.

■ *TIP* The development of knickpoints requires *stability* in environmental processes (tectonic and climatic) over millions of years. Given the dynamic nature of environmental systems, it is extremely difficult to identify knickpoints with any certainty.

knock and lochan topography: glacial eroded landscapes of low relief studded with thousands of small lakes and rocky outcrops.

■ Knock and lochan topography is found in areas of resistant rock and low relief affected by continental glaciation, where *ice sheets* have abraded hollows and rounded rocky outcrops. The lakes and ridges of knock and lochan landscapes often have a clear alignment, with their long axes oriented in the direction of ice flow.

■ *e.g.* Much of the Laurentian Shield of northern Canada has knock and lochan topography with lakes and ridges aligned roughly north–south.

■ *TIP* Knock and lochan topography should remind you that continental glaciation often has very different erosional effects compared to alpine glaciation, which is confined to valleys in mountainous areas.

labour costs: cost of wages, pension contributions, health insurance etc. paid by an employer to workers.

▨ Labour costs are a significant part of total costs in many economic activities. Some activities locate where labour costs are low. The *global shift* of manufacturing industry is partly explained by a search for lower labour costs.

▨ *e.g.* the location of hundreds of Hong Kong manufacturing businesses in the Pearl River delta in eastern China in the last 15 years.

▨ *TIP* You should make a distinction between labour costs and *unit labour costs*. The latter consider the productivity of labour as well as labour costs.

labour-intensive industry: industry where *labour costs* are a large proportion of total costs.

▨ Labour-intensive industries often choose locations that minimise labour costs.

▨ *e.g.* the clothing industry.

lag time: interval between maximum precipitation intensity and maximum discharge of a stream or river (see *hydrograph*).

▨ Lag times are influenced by fixed drainage basin characteristics (e.g. geology, soils, slopes, vegetation cover, drainage density) and variable factors (e.g. soil moisture, snow cover, *precipitation* amount and intensity, *evapotranspiration*).

▨ *TIP* Rivers with short lag times are described as 'flashy'. They rise and fall rapidly and are most likely to flood.

lahar: *mudflow* or debris flow originating on a *volcano*.

▨ Lahars occur when heavy rainfall or rapid snowmelt transports huge amounts of loose volcanic ash from the slopes of a volcano. Lahars are high-density, fast-moving debris flows and are very destructive.

▨ *e.g.* Lahars triggered by the eruption of Nevado del Ruiz in Colombia in 1985 killed more than 20,000 people.

laminar flow: smooth flow of water in a river channel where the water molecules slide across each other.

land degradation: deterioration in the suitability of land for agriculture that results from *soil erosion, desertification* and *salinisation*.

▨ Land degradation is most severe in drylands and is the outcome of poor land management and the misuse of soil, water and vegetation resources.

TIP It is often wrongly assumed that land degradation is confined to LEDCs. In fact, land degradation through soil erosion is a major problem throughout the economically developed world.

land reform: government-organised redistribution of agricultural land.

The motivation behind land reform is usually economic or political. Land reform may improve farming efficiency by consolidating small, scattered parcels of land into larger, single blocks. It may also involve the forced break-up of large estates and the redistribution of land to small farmers.

e.g. Land reform began in Taiwan in 1951 with the government compulsorily purchasing larger holdings (6 ha of wet rice land and 12 ha of dry). This land was then provided to purchasers on easy credit terms. Land reform was highly successful and led to substantial increases in agricultural output.

landslide: rapid downslope movement of an unsaturated *regolith* as a coherent mass, across a well-defined slide plain.

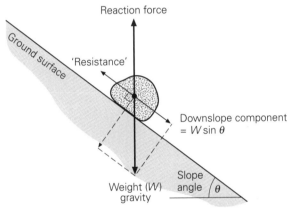

Force of gravity acting on a slope particle

Landslides occur when the downslope forces of gravity and the mass of material on a slope exceed the frictional resistance to movement. Landslides may be classified according to the shape of their slide planes. Rotational slides (or slumps) occur on curved slide planes. Translational slides move across straight (or planar) slide planes.

e.g. the Mam Tor landslides in the Peak District.

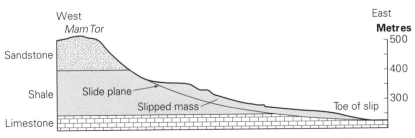

Major features of the Mam Tor landslip, Derbyshire

lapse rate: decrease of temperature with altitude (see *adiabatic cooling* and *environmental lapse rate*).

laterisation: soil-forming process in humid tropical environments with high *precipitation*.

■ Silica and humus are washed from the surface soil horizons, which become enriched with insoluble oxides of iron and aluminium.

■ *TIP* Laterisation is in some respects the opposite of podzolisation (see *podzol*). In podzolisation it is the oxides or iron and aluminium that are mobilised, forming a silica-rich horizon near the surface.

laterite: cemented layer of iron and aluminium oxides that forms in the upper part of soils in humid tropical climates, where soils undergo seasonal wetting and drying.

lava: hot liquid rock extruded on to the Earth's surface and the rocks solidified from it.

■ *e.g. basalt* lava that may solidify to form a smooth ropy surface (*pahoehoe*) or a rough clinkery surface (*aa*).

lava plateau: plateau formed by huge extrusions of lava built up in successive layers over thousands of years.

■ Lava plateaux often have distinctive stepped slope profiles known as 'trappe' topography. The steps represent individual lava flows, each with a slightly different lithology.

■ *e.g.* the Antrim Plateau in Northern Ireland formed by Tertiary volcanic activity.

leaching: transport of soluble minerals downwards through the *soil profile* by the soil water.

■ Leaching occurs when *precipitation* exceeds *evapotranspiration,* giving a net downward movement of water within the soil profile. Leaching creates an acidic environment and depletes the surface soil horizons of nutrients and humus.

■ *TIP* It is easy to confuse leaching and *eluviation.* Leaching is the removal of minerals in solution; eluviation is the downwashing of solid particles.

LEDCs: see *less economically developed countries*.

Lee's migration model: model that explains *migration* in terms of the positive and negative attributes of places of origin and destination and the intervening obstacles between them.

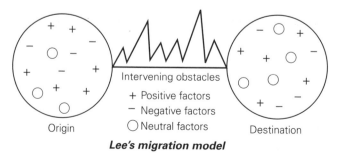

Lee's migration model

■ According to the model, a potential migrant assesses the place utility or value of his or her current residence and compares it with an intended destination. If a migrant's perception of the place utility of a destination exceeds that of their place of residence (taking into account both positive and negative attributes), migration is likely occur. However, a third factor — intervening obstacles such as poor communications and international borders — has to be taken into account. If these obstacles are too great, migration may not occur.

■ *TIP* Lee's model is a useful development of the simpler *push–pull* model. Through the concepts of place utility, *perception* and intervening obstacles, it recognises the importance of individual decision-making.

less economically developed countries (LEDCs): the world's poorer countries.

■ LEDCs have an economic profile that includes relatively low incomes per capita, low GDP per capita, low value of trade per capita and an overdependence on low-productivity agriculture.

■ *TIP* Most countries are LEDCs (see also *more economically developed countries*, MEDCs). However, there is no simple dichotomy of LEDCs and MEDCs. Rather, there is a continuum of countries varying from least developed (e.g. Sierra Leone) to most developed (e.g. USA).

Less Favoured Areas (LFAs): difficult farming environments in the EU, such as uplands and drylands, where farmers receive livestock subsidies from the EU's structural funds.

■ Money is available in LFAs to improve agriculture and to secure the survival of rural communities.

■ *e.g.* Highlands of Scotland.

■ *TIP* You should make the connection between livestock subsidies in LFAs and land degradation. Headage payments (subsidies per head of livestock) encourage overstocking, which leads to overgrazing and *soil erosion*.

levée: natural or artificial embankment bordering a river channel on a *flood plain*.

■ Natural levées are formed from the deposition of suspended sediment when a river floods. As flood water spills out of the channel, there is an immediate reduction in velocity. Deposition of the river's suspended *load* occurs, and is most concentrated around the edges of the channel.

■ *TIP* Levées can increase the flood risk. At high discharge, rivers may flow in channels confined by levées with the water level above the flood plain. In this situation, if a levée bursts, catastrophic floods can result.

life expectancy: see *mortality*.

lithosere: *plant succession* on a bare rock surface.

■ Lithoseres are a type of *xerosere* and are common in recently deglaciated areas. Lack of moisture on exposed rock surfaces is the main problem for plants. Pioneer colonisers include lichens and mosses. They provide organic debris which aids moisture retention and thus allows grasses and herbaceous plants to invade.

■ *e.g.* In deglaciated areas in Alaska, successional stages include lichen and mosses, mountain avens, dwarf birch and willow, conifers, silver birch and aspen.

lithosphere: Earth's crust and the immediate underlying part of the *mantle*.

- The crust and lithosphere comprise a single unit. Tectonic plates (see *plate tectonics*) are made of both crust and lithosphere.

load: rock particles and minerals transported by a river by suspension, *saltation*, traction and *solution* (see *bedload*).

- A river's load comes from *erosion* of the river's channel and valley side and from *weathering* and *mass movement* on valley slopes. The solution load is carried continuously, but the suspended load and bedload only intermittently and at high flow. The solution load comprises dissolved minerals such as calcium carbonate. The suspended load consists of tiny particles of silt and clay entrained in the flow. Bedload (pebbles, cobbles and boulders) is too heavy to be entrained. It rolls and slides along the river bed.

- *TIP* It is worth emphasising that rivers do two things: they transport water and sediment. The shape of river channels, both in cross-section and planform, is adjusted not only to *bankfull* discharge, but also to the river's sediment load. See *braiding*.

localisation economies: see *external economies* and *agglomeration economies*.

location quotient: proportion of the workforce in a locality employed in a particular economic activity, compared to the national proportion.

- A location quotient of more than 1 means that an economic activity is relatively more important locally than nationally. Where the location quotient is less than 1, the economic activity has relatively less importance locally than nationally. A location quotient of 1 means that local representation of the economic activity is comparable with the national representation.

- *e.g.* The motor vehicle industry in the West Midlands of England has a location quotient of 3.65. This suggests that the motor vehicle industry is three and a half times more important in the West Midlands economy than it is in the UK as a whole.

- *TIP* Location quotients can be derived from data other than employment. For instance, the proportion of GDP generated by an economic activity locally and nationally could be used instead.

loess: wind-blown deposit of fine particles and dust that weathers to form a fertile but easily eroded soil.

- Loess is derived from fine *glacio-fluvial deposits* that were widespread in Europe and North America at the end of the last *glacial*.

- *e.g.* the Yellow River basin in China. The Yellow River gets its name from the eroded loess transported by the river.

longshore drift: lateral migration of beach material in a preferred direction along a coastline.

- Longshore drift occurs when waves strike the coast obliquely (i.e. wave *refraction* is not complete). The result is a zigzag movement of sand and shingle along beaches and a current that runs parallel to the coast and transports sand in the nearshore zone. Longshore drift produces drift-aligned beaches including *spits* and *barrier beach islands*.

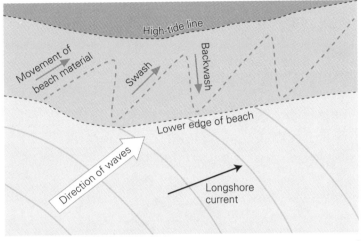

Longshore drift: the flow of coastal sediment produced by wave and current action when waves approach at an angle to the coastline

- ▨ *e.g.* the east–west longshore drift in north Norfolk is responsible for Blakeney Point (a spit) and Scolt Head Island (a barrier beach island).
- ▨ *TIP* Don't assume that all spits (or barrier beaches) have grown by longshore drift. The incontrovertible evidence for longshore drift is lateral extension shown by shingle ridges or recurves (see *recurved lateral*). Beaches that are straight, such as Chesil and Slapton Sands, are not thought to have developed by longshore movement only.

magma: hot liquid rock beneath the Earth's surface.

magma chamber: reservoir of *magma* beneath a *volcano*.

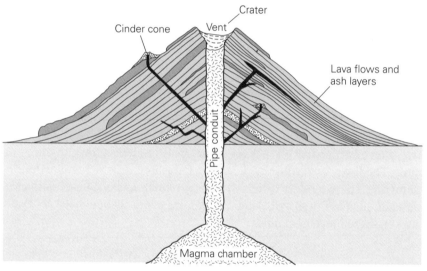

Magma chamber beneath a strato-volcano

■ Magma from the *mantle* fills the magma chamber before an eruption. This process is detectable by changes in gravity and land elevation (inflation) at the surface.

malnutrition: lack of adequate nutrition caused by an unbalanced diet.

■ Malnutrition is widespread in LEDCs and also occurs among the poorest socio-economic groups in MEDCs. People suffering from malnutrition lack nutrients and protein in their diets. Malnutrition in children often impairs mental development and physical growth.

■ *TIP* Malnutrition is not the same as *undernutrition*. Malnourished people often have an adequate calorie intake; they simply do not have enough of the right sorts of food to remain healthy.

Malthus' theory: theory that a rapidly growing population will eventually outstrip the growth of its food supplies, leading to a population crash.

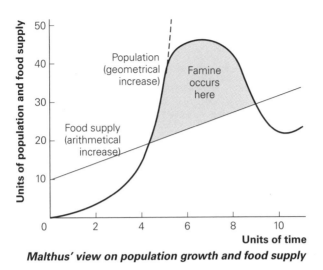

Malthus' view on population growth and food supply

■ Thomas Malthus wrote his essay on population in the late eighteenth century. It was based on the experience of demographic change in England. At that time, England's population was undergoing unprecedented expansion owing to high fertility and declining *mortality*. Malthus argued that the growth in food production would not keep pace with population growth. He believed that unless people had fewer children, the outcome would be catastrophic mortality through starvation, disease and war.

■ *TIP* The population crash predicted by Malthus did not occur, despite a threefold increase in population in Britain during the nineteenth century. The fundamental idea that food output could not keep pace with population growth proved wrong. However, Malthusian ideas remain popular (neo-Malthusians). Biologists such as Robert Ehrlich argue that long-term population growth is unsustainable, and that ultimately Malthus' prognosis will prove accurate.

managed retreat: approach to coastal management that no longer seeks to protect some low-lying coastal areas from flooding.

■ Managed retreat (and managed realignment) is an increasingly popular alternative to *hard engineering*. The cost of maintaining sea defences to protect agricultural land in the face of rising sea level (the result of *global warming*) is prohibitive. Building ever-higher *sea walls* and embankments is also unsustainable. Managed retreat allows the sea to flood lowland coasts, creating natural protection through the formation of *mudflats* and *salt marshes*, and establishing a new line of defence inland. As well as being cost-effective, managed retreat has obvious environmental benefits.

■ *e.g.* Managed retreat is already an established strategy for coastal management along the sparsely populated coast of Essex in southeast England.

■ *TIP* Managed retreat is a controversial policy and arouses strong opposition from farmers and landowners. You should be aware of the arguments for and against managed retreat and develop your own views on the issue.

Mann's model: urban structure model that incorporates zonal and sectoral arrangements of land use.

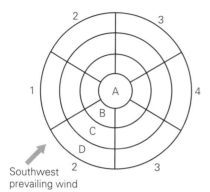

1 Middle income residents
2 Lower middle income residents
3 Lower income and council houses
4 Industry and lowest quality houses
A Central business district
B Nineteenth-century houses, high densities, houses in need of repair, some redevelopment and renovation. Factories found here as well
C Sectors 1 and 2, old, large houses. Sectors 3 and 4, small terraced houses
D Recent housing development (since 1918)

Sectors 1 and 2 are thought to be more pleasant places to live than 3 and 4 because the latter have to suffer the pollution from the city carried by the prevailing wind.

Mann's structure model of a typical British city

■ Mann's model was based on the structure of British cities. Higher-income groups locate on the upwind (west) side of the city where air pollution is lowest. The model also takes account of the importance of local authority housing in British cities.

■ *e.g.* The model was originally devised for Huddersfield, West Yorkshire.

■ *TIP* Mann's model reminds us that general urban structure models (e.g. *Burgess, Hoyt*) that are based on US cities provide only limited insight into city structure in other MEDCs. Urban structure is strongly influenced by society and history.

mantle: that part of the Earth's interior between the crust and the core.

■ The mantle forms over 80% of the Earth's volume. Most of the mantle is solid rock with minerals of high density dominated by magnesium and iron. The upper part of the mantle (the asthenosphere) has plastic properties that allow it to flow under pressure. This movement, powered by convection currents, is responsible for plate movement and *continental drift*.

maquiladora: branch factories located in Mexico in the USA–Mexico border zone, which are owned by foreign companies.

■ Maquiladora are the result of *foreign direct investment* mainly by US, Japanese and other east Asian *transnational corporations* in the past 20 years. They specialise in *labour-intensive industries* such as consumer electronics and textiles. The main attractions of the border region include low labour costs, easy access to the US market, less stringent environmental controls and the border's status as a free trade zone.

■ *TIP* Mexico's maquiladora provide an excellent example of the *global shift* of manufacturing from MEDCs to LEDCs.

market gardening (also called 'horticulture'): capital- and labour-intensive type of agriculture in MEDCs that specialises in the production of high-value salad crops, flowers and soft fruit.

▒ Market gardening is usually found on smallholdings and a large part of production often takes place in the controlled environments of glasshouses and cloches. Market gardening is a high input–high output enterprise.

▒ *e.g.* the bulb-growing area between Haarlem and Leiden in the Netherlands.

mass balance: net gain or loss of snow and ice by a *glacier* during a year.

▒ Glaciers are systems with inputs of snow (accumulation) and outputs of meltwater and water vapour (*ablation*). A positive mass balance (i.e. input exceeds output) leads to glacier advance. A negative mass balance results in glacier retreat. Most modern glaciers have a negative mass balance.

mass movement (also called 'mass wasting'): downhill transference of slope materials moving as a coherent body.

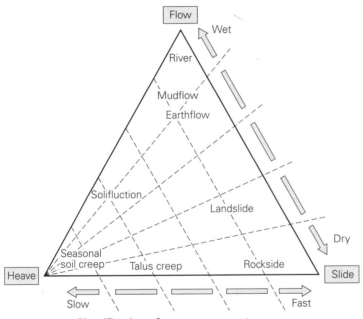

Classification of mass movement processes

▒ There are three types of mass movement: slides, flows and heaves. This classification is based on the speed of movement and the amount of moisture in the slope materials. Mass movements are influenced by slope angle, the weight (mass) of material on a slope and the coherence of the slope materials. The most common triggers to mass movement are an increase in moisture levels in slope materials following heavy *precipitation*; undercutting (by a river or wave action) at the slope foot; and the *weathering* of slope materials.

▒ *e.g.* cliff collapse at Beachy Head, Sussex, on 12 January 1999. The causes of this rockfall (in chalk) were marine *erosion* at the cliff base, freeze–thaw weathering and the saturated state of the chalk.

mass production: large-scale manufacturing of standardised items based on long production runs and *economies of scale*.

▓ Mass production lowers unit costs and thus maximises market potential. There is a rigid division of labour, with workers often performing short-cycle repetitive tasks.

▓ *e.g.* volume car production in the motor vehicle industry.

▓ *TIP* The opposite of mass production is customisation, where items are manufactured to suit individual consumer demand. Customisation demands a more *flexible production* system.

mass wasting: see *mass movement*.

meander: river channel with a sinuous planform.

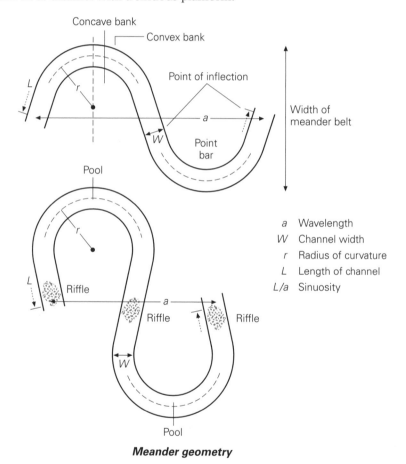

Meander geometry

▓ Most river channels have a tendency to meander. The degree of meandering (or sinuosity) is measured by the ratio of channel distance between two points and the straight-line distance between these points. A channel is meandering if the sinuosity ratio is equal to or exceeds 1.5. Meandering rivers usually have relatively high power and coherent silt-clay banks. The tendency to meander may be related to frictional resistance to flow between the water and the channel bed and banks (even in straight channels, water follows a sinuous path). It may also represent an equilibrium condition (i.e. if a river has excess power, it erodes its channel into a meandering form, thus decreasing its average gradient and expending surplus energy).

■ *TIP* There is no clear explanation for meanders and questions on this topic are unlikely at AS and A-level. However, that still leaves plenty of scope for the discussion of meanders (e.g. how you would measure them, factors associated with meandering, flow characteristics (including velocities) in a meander, fluvial erosion and deposition).

meander terrace: unpaired river terraces along the sides of a flood plain.

■ Meander terraces are the remnants of an old *flood plain* surface. As a river meanders across its flood plain, it erodes vertically as well as laterally. Remnants of the original flood plain survive as terraces, though not at the same level. Meander terraces often develop as a result of an increase in river discharge following climatic change.

■ *TIP* Unlike *rejuvenation terraces*, meander terraces do not match with other terraces on the opposite side of the valley. This tells us that incision (i.e. down-cutting) occurred relatively slowly.

measures of central tendency: descriptive statistical measures that represent a data set by a middle value.

■ There are three measures of central tendency: mean, median and mode. The arithmetic mean or average is a useful measure for data sets that follow a *normal frequency distribution* and have no extreme values. The median is the middle value of a data set, where the values are arranged in rank order. Unlike the mean, the median cannot be used in further calculations, but is a better summary of data that have a *skewed frequency distribution* or contain extreme values. The mode is the data class in a frequency table or histogram that has the most values. It has similar advantages to the median, but being a range of values (rather than a single value) is less useful.

■ *e.g.* In a country like Saudi Arabia, incomes are highly skewed: the vast majority of people are relatively poor; a few people are fabulously wealthy. The mean income for the country is inflated by the wealthy elite, giving an inaccurate picture of human well-being. The median is not affected by the small number of people with very high incomes and thus provides a more accurate summary of income distribution.

mechanical weathering: see *physical weathering*.

MEDCs: see *more economically developed countries*.

meltwater: streams and rivers fed by water from melting *glaciers*.

■ Meltwater streams are important agents of transport, especially during phases of *deglaciation*. They have high and variable discharge, carry large sediment *loads* and often flow under hydrostatic pressure within glaciers. Meltwater streams and rivers often flow in braided channels and through deposition are responsible for glacio-fluvial landforms such as *eskers, kames, kame terraces* and *sandar*.

■ *TIP* Many rivers in northern Britain were meltwater rivers during the long period of deglaciation at the end of the last *glacial*. These rivers infilled valleys with coarse debris (*valley trains*) that today form the lower sequence of deposits of many *flood plains*. This reminds us that many landforms are fossil features and owe their form to processes no longer operating today.

metamorphic rock: rock that has been altered either by high temperature or high pressure or both.

■ Contact metamorphism occurs when rocks are in contact with large masses of molten *igneous rock*. The rocks metamorphosed in this way form a zone around the igneous mass known as an aureole. High pressure increases the density of minerals, creates new minerals and reorientates minerals at right angles to the direction of pressure.

■ *e.g.* sugar limestone (semi-metamorphosed marble) formed by contact between limestone and the Great Whin Sill on Cronkley Fell, Upper Teesdale. Dalradian schists in northern Scotland are the result of pressure metamorphism.

microclimate: local climates whose characteristics have been influenced by slopes, vegetation, land use and other surfaces.

■ Factors such as relief and land use modify energy exchanges, the *water cycle* and airflow at a local scale. The result is local climates whose temperature, *precipitation* and airflow characteristics differ significantly from the regional climate.

■ *e.g.* the *heat island* effect of large urban areas.

mid-ocean ridge: boundary between two divergent oceanic plates which comprises two parallel mountain ridges separated by a *graben* (rift valley).

■ Mid-ocean ridges are almost entirely submarine features. They are located on *constructive plate boundaries* (see *seafloor spreading*), where *magma* rises to the ocean floor and forms new crust. This movement leads to volcanic activity, with associated *faults* and *earthquakes*.

■ *e.g.* the mid-Atlantic ridge, which in Iceland rises above sea level to form an impressive rift valley (Thingvellir) with *volcanoes* such as Hekla and Skjaldbreidar forming adjacent ridges.

migration: movement of people that involves a permanent or semi-permanent change of residence.

■ See *emigration* and *immigration*.

monoculture: agricultural system in which a single crop is grown continuously in the same field.

■ Monoculture is a highly specialised agriculture system that has both ecological and economic drawbacks (e.g. it exhausts soil fertility, increases the risks from pests and diseases and threatens a farmer's income if crop prices fall). However, in a commercial system, large-scale cultivation of a single crop may be highly profitable, allowing *economies of scale*.

e.g. the cultivation of wheat on the Canadian prairies.

TIP The opposite farming system to monoculture is polyculture.

moraine: mounds and ridges formed from *boulder clay* (till).

Most moraines have one of two origins: melt-out deposits formed as *glaciers* decayed, leaving behind mounds of unsorted debris; or deposits formed by moving ice at the base of the glacier. *Hummocky moraines* are melt-out deposits. They lack any clear fabric (i.e. the long axes of their larger particles have no preferred orientation) and have a conical shape. Moraines formed by moving ice often have a streamlined shape (e.g. *drumlins*), with the long axes of their larger particles oriented in the direction of ice flow.

TIP The fabric of moraines is not an absolute indication of the conditions in which they formed. After deposition, slope processes (e.g. sliding, heaving) may destroy the original fabric.

more economically developed countries (MEDCs): world's richer countries.

MEDCs have an economic profile that includes high incomes per capita, high GDP per capita, high value of trade per capita and a sophisticated economy based on high added value manufacturing, *quaternary* and *quinary* services.

TIP See also *less economically developed countries (LEDCs)*.

mortality: occurrence of deaths.

There are several measures of mortality. The *crude death rate* (CDR) is the most common measure of mortality. However, like the *crude birth rate* (CBR), the CDR is strongly affected by age structure. Age-specific mortality rates are the number of deaths in a given age group in a year. Life expectancy at each age is the number of years of life expected for each of the survivors at any given age. Both age-specific mortality and life expectancy are more accurate indicators of mortality than the CDR.

mudflats: extensive zone of clay and silt in the *inter-tidal area*, exposed for a few hours on each tidal cycle.

Mudflats develop close to the low water mark and are therefore inundated for much of the time. They form in low-energy environments such as estuaries, from the deposition of tiny particles transported by rivers and tidal currents. The lowest mudflats have no plant cover; higher mudflats support pioneer species (see *pioneer community*) such as cord grass (Spartina) and glasswort (Salicornia). These plants encourage sedimentation, which eventually leads to the formation of *salt marsh*.

e.g. large areas of mudflats on the south shore of Ribble Estuary between Preston and Southport.

mudflow: flows of water-saturated clay and silt-sized particles that result from periods of heavy rain or a sudden thaw.

Mudflows may have a water content up to 30%. They are often found in areas of sparse vegetation (e.g. drylands) and frequently form large fans and lobes on lower ground with gentler slopes. *Lahars* are a type of mudflow.

TIP There is an important and often overlooked difference between *mass* *movement* flows and slides. In a flow, the velocity decreases with depth, whereas in slides velocity is uniform throughout the sliding mass.

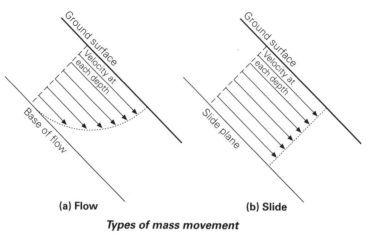

(a) Flow **(b) Slide**

Types of mass movement

mudslide: similar to *mudflow* except that the *regolith* moves as a coherent mass across a clearly defined slide plane.
■ *e.g.* Black Ven, Dorset.

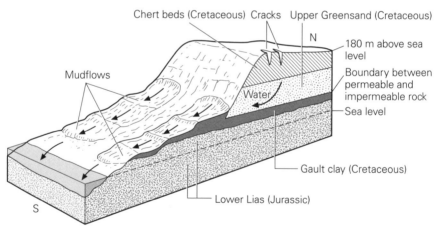

The geology of the landslips and mudflows at Black Ven, Dorset

multinational: see *transnational corporation*.

multiple retailer: large retailing chain with outlets in many different shopping centres.
■ The largest multiples are supermarket giants such as Tesco and Sainsbury's and high street retailers such as Marks and Spencer, and Boots. Multiples dominate retailing in the UK and their share of the market has grown at the expense of *independent retailers* in the past 30 years.

multiplier effect: concept that an initial investment in an economic activity in a region has beneficial knock-on effects elsewhere in the regional economy.

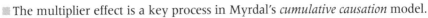

- The multiplier effect is a key process in Myrdal's *cumulative causation* model.
- *e.g.* Investment by Toyota in its second EU car assembly plant at Valenciennes in 2001 created not only direct employment for the 2,000 workers in the plant, but also an estimated 5,000 jobs in parts suppliers in the Nord-Pas-de-Calais region. Money injected into the regional economy through wages to car workers will have further multiplier effects on services (e.g. retailing).

nappe: folded strata that have been pushed forward across a *thrust fault*.

■ Nappes are the result of extreme pressure that causes the upper part of a fold to shear (see *folding*). Further pressure then causes the upper part of the fold to move forward across this shear plane or thrust fault.

National Park: large tract of countryside of outstanding environmental quality created by government legislation and protected against inappropriate development.

■ The first National Park was designated in the USA in 1872. Today more than 120 countries have National Parks. National parks vary in character. In countries such as Canada and Kenya, they are often *wilderness areas*. In England and Wales, National Parks contain significant population, settlement and economic activities. Most National Parks are government funded. The priorities of National Parks are: (a) to protect and conserve landscapes and ecosystems; (b) to promote recreation and leisure activities by making the parks accessible to the public. Most National Parks face critical and often conflicting issues of resource use, conservation and *sustainability*.

■ *e.g.* Yellowstone, Wyoming, the world's first National Park.

■ *TIP* You should be aware that the two primary aims of National Parks — conservation and promoting public access — are often conflicting. The nature of these conflicts, the management responses and their effectiveness is an important focus of study at AS and A-level.

natural population change: difference between the number of births and deaths in a country or region in a year.

■ Natural population increase occurs when the *crude birth rate* (CBR) exceeds the *crude death rate* (CDR). Natural population decrease is when the CDR exceeds the CBR. Natural population change is usually expressed as a percentage per year.

■ *e.g.* In 1997 Brazil's CBR was 20 per 1,000; its CDR was 9 per 1,000. Natural increase was therefore 20 – 9 or 11 per 1,000, which is 1.1% per year. Ukraine in 1997 had a CBR of 12 per 1,000 and a CDR of 15 per 1,000, and experienced a natural decrease of 3 per 1,000 or 0.3% over the year.

■ *TIP* Natural increase is one of two ways that a population can grow: the other is through a net migrational gain. Remember that in the absence of any migration, natural increase results in population growth and natural decrease results in population fall.

nature reserves: small conservation areas protected because of their rare or valuable ecology and geology.

■ Nature reserves in the UK cover important habitats such as woodland, grassland, wetland and sand dunes. There is usually some management of nature reserves. In the UK, responsibility for reserves rests with various organisations including the government (e.g. national nature reserves) and the county wildlife trusts.

■ *e.g.* Wicken Fen, Cambridgeshire, the UK's oldest nature reserve. Wicken is a wetland habitat owned and managed by the National Trust.

neap tide: low tidal range that occurs twice every lunar month.

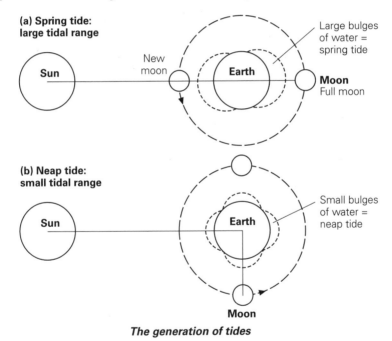

The generation of tides

■ Neap tides occur when the sun and moon (the two tide-raising bodies) are at right angles to each other. In this position they exert the weakest gravitational pull and therefore raise the lowest tides.

nearest neighbour analysis: statistical technique that compares the actual spatial distribution of a number of points with the pattern that would exist if the points were distributed randomly.

■ Nearest neighbour analysis is an objective technique for assessing clustering, randomness and uniformity in a point pattern.

$$R_n = 2\overline{d}\sqrt{\frac{n}{A}}$$

where $\bar{d}$ = mean distance between points

A = area in which points are distributed

n = the number of points

Values of R_n range from zero, when all the points are clustered, to 2.15 when the points have their maximum spacing. A random distribution has an R_n value of 1.

■ *TIP* Nearest neighbour analysis — like many statistical techniques — is not as objective as you might think. When using nearest neighbour analysis, you will have to decide on the boundaries that delimit the area of the pattern, and the scale of the analysis. Both can exert a major influence on the outcome.

negative correlation: see *correlation*.

negative feedback: process of self-regulation within a system.

■ Negative feedback is an automatic response to change which restores a system to balance.

■ *e.g.* localised *erosion* of a river bank overloads the river with sediment. The river deposits the sediment in its channel. This causes a localised steepening of channel gradient, which gives the river increased power to transport the sediment. The system is thus restored to balance; the transport of sediment on this reach now equals the input by erosion.

negative skew: see *skewed frequency distribution*.

net migrational change: difference between the number of people moving permanently into an area and out of an area.

■ A net migrational gain is when more people move into an area than move out. A net migrational loss occurs when the number moving out exceeds the number moving in.

■ *TIP* In most MEDCs, regional variations in *crude birth rates* and *crude death rates* are small. In these countries, you can assume that regional differences in population change largely result from net migrational gains and losses.

net primary production (NPP): solar energy converted in photosynthesis to chemical energy by plants, minus energy losses due to respiration.

■ Npp is usually measured in g m^{-2} per year. It represents the total amount of usable organic materials available to consumer organisms in an *ecosystem* (see *food chain*). NPP varies from one ecosystem to another.

■ *e.g.* *Coral reefs* and *estuaries* are the world's most productive ecosystems. NPP in these ecosystems averages nearly 2,000 g m^{-2} per year. At the opposite end of the scale, *deserts* are least productive, with npps as low as 3 g m^{-2} per year.

neve: another name for *firn*.

newly industrialising country (NIC): country that in the past 30 years or so has undergone rapid and successful industrialisation.

■ The term 'NIC' has mainly been used to describe the four *Asian 'tiger'* economies: Taiwan, South Korea, Singapore and Hong Kong. The industrialisation strategy followed by these NICs has varied. South Korea's industrialisation was government led, and dominated by very large conglomerates known as chaebols (e.g. Samsung, Daewoo). In Taiwan, state influence was less prominent and centred on thousands of small businesses. The industrial success of NICs was based on export-oriented industries. Today many NIC industries are relocating overseas to source cheaper labour and materials, and avoid import barriers. The next generation of NICs will probably include Malaysia, Thailand and Brazil.

NIC: see *newly industrialising country.*

nitrate pollution: excessive concentrations of nitrates in streams, rivers and groundwater that damage aquatic life and contaminate drinking water.

■ Nitrate pollution is mainly caused by the use of nitrate fertilisers in areas of commercial arable farming. Nitrates are soluble and easily *leached* from the soil. Runoff transfers nitrates into streams and rivers and leads to *eutrophication.* Groundwater polluted by nitrates is a threat to human health, being associated with hypertension and 'blue baby' syndrome. In some of the worst-affected areas of the UK, farmers receive subsidies to compensate them for cutting back on nitrate inputs.

■ *e.g.* Many arable areas in East Anglia have suffered severe nitrate pollution through excessive use of chemical fertilisers.

nivation: breakdown of rocks and the transport of rock debris which takes place beneath a patch of melting snow.

■ Nivation is a combination of processes associated with meltwater beneath snow patches. *Frost weathering*, *gelifluction* and meltwater flow all contribute to nivation, which produces shallow hollows on hill slopes. It is thought that these nivation hollows may be the first stage in the development of *cirques* or corries.

nomadic herding: livestock farming that involves the circular migration of animals and herdsmen in search of pasture and water.

■ Nomadic herding is a system of farming in environments where climatic conditions will not sustain sedentary agriculture. The resources needed to sustain livestock are spread over a wide area. Herdsmen exploit them by following traditional circular routes. Their movements are timed to coincide with the availability of pasture and water. Nomadic herding is found in tropical semi-arid, mountainous and sub-arctic environments.

■ *e.g.* the Tuareg cattle and camel herders of Yatanga (Burkina Faso).

■ *TIP* Despite the attempts of many governments to sedentarise nomadic groups, nomadic herding remains a highly successful means of exploiting the limited resources of marginal environments. The fact that nomadic herding has survived for thousands of years also tells us that it is a sustainable farming system.

non-renewable resources: resources such as *fossil fuels*, mineral ores and soils that once used cannot be replaced.

■ The consumption of non-renewables raises concerns about future supplies and environmental pollution.

■ *e.g.* The consumption of oil contributes to atmospheric pollution and *global warming* and depletes reserves. Ultimately (and possibly within the next 50 years), oil resources will run out.

normal fault: almost vertical displacement of rocks along a fault plane caused by tensional forces in the Earth's crust (see *fault*).

normal frequency distribution: data set that has a bell-shaped symmetrical distribution around the arithmetic mean.

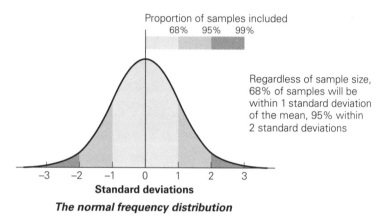

The normal frequency distribution

■ The normal frequency distribution has similar values for mean, median and mode. Approximately 68% of values in a normal distribution lie within 1 standard deviation of the mean, and around 95% of values lie within 2 standard deviations of the mean. Several important statistical tests (e.g. t-test, analysis of variance) assume that data are taken from *populations* with a normal distribution.

■ *TIP* If you decide to use statistical tests in project work, it is safer to use tests such as Spearman's rank *correlation*, the *U-test* and *chi-squared* that make no assumptions about the data's frequency distribution.

NPP: see *net primary production*.

nucleated settlement pattern: spatial distribution of rural settlement dominated by villages.

■ Nucleated settlement patterns often developed in areas of chalk and limestone where surface water is scarce. Villages develop at wet-point sites around springs and streams. Similar nucleated patterns also developed in lowland Britain where the feudal system and communal agriculture operated in the Middle Ages. Communal agriculture, with no individual land ownership, meant that peasant farmers lived in village settlements rather than isolated farms.

■ *TIP* Nucleated settlement patterns often cause problems because they are confused with *nucleated villages*. A settlement pattern covers a system of settlements in a region and does not refer to individual settlements.

nucleated village: village with a compact form, where farms, houses and other buildings are clustered around a central green, square, church etc.

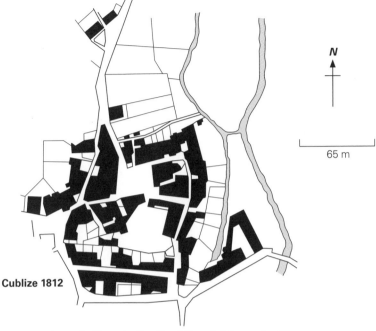

Cublize 1812

Nucleated village in the Haut Beaujolais, central France

▨ Villages have a variety of planforms. Circular, square and rectangular villages are usually nucleated. Villages with ribbon-like forms, arranged along a road or street, are non-nucleated.

null hypothesis: hypothesis of 'no difference' or 'no association' between two or more sets of data.

▨ The null hypothesis is the initial proposition set up in scientific enquiry. If the null hypothesis is proved invalid, it is replaced by the alternative research hypothesis. In geography, the research hypothesis is usually accepted if it is significant at the 95% (and above) confidence level.

▨ *e.g.* There is no significant difference in channel width at upstream and downstream sites on a river.

nunatak: mountain whose higher elevations project above surrounding *ice sheets*.

▨ In the British Isles at various times during the Devensian *glacial*, the highest peaks would have been free of ice. These exposed peaks would have experienced severe *frost weathering*.

▨ *e.g.* the Transantarctic Mountains.

nutrient cycle: continuous movement of mineral nutrients between the soil, atmosphere and living organisms.

▨ The nutrient cycle is a vital flow in natural *ecosystems*. Rocks are the principal source of most nutrients (e.g. calcium, potassium) that are released by *weathering*. The atmosphere also plays an important role in the cycling of nutrients such as nitrogen and carbon. Nutrients enter the biotic component of ecosystems through plant roots. On the death of plants and other organisms, decomposers release these nutrients and make them available for recycling.

■ *e.g.* Shifting cultivators exploit the nutrient cycle in tropical rainforest by making clearings in the forest, burning trees and branches and growing crops on the enriched soil. Cultivation soon depletes the soil's nutrient store, leading to abandonment of plots. It takes 20 or 30 years for the nutrient cycle to re-establish itself fully.

■ *TIP* It is the nutrient cycle, along with the flow of energy in ecosystems, that binds the physical and biotic components of ecosystems together. Without the efficient cycling of mineral nutrients, ecosystems would not be sustainable.

Objective 1 and 2 areas: urban and industrial areas targeted for financial assistance by the EU's regional policies.

▪ Objective 1 areas are defined as 'substantially lagging behind the rest of Europe'. They have a GDP per head that is less than 75% of the EU average. EU money is available in Objective 1 areas for improving competitiveness and promoting new businesses and innovation. Objective 2 areas have been seriously affected by industrial decline. They have unemployment levels above the EU average and an excessive dependence on employment in industry. They have also suffered an absolute fall in the number of jobs in industry in recent years.

▪ **e.g.** South Yorkshire and Cornwall have Objective 1 status. Several coalfield areas in the UK qualify for Objective 2 status.

▪ **TIP** EU regional policies are becoming more important than national regional policies. In addition, through the influence of the EU, national regional policies are converging.

occlusion: type of front in a *depression* where the *warm sector* is lifted above the ground.

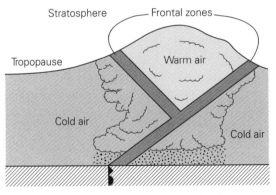

Cross-section through an occlusion

▪ Occlusions develop when the *cold front* catches up with the *warm front*, lifting the air in the warm sector above the ground. Air aloft continues to rise, producing a mass of cloud and prolonged *precipitation*.

TIP Occlusions are associated with the later stages of the life cycle of depressions. Often they are slow moving, causing lengthy spells of heavy precipitation.

oceanicity: climatic conditions dominated by the influence of oceans.

Oceanicity is the opposite of *continentality*. The oceans have a moderating influence on temperatures in middle and high latitudes. In winter they release their accumulated heat slowly. This raises temperatures well above the average for the latitude. In summer they have the opposite effect, heating up slowly and depressing temperatures below the latitudinal average. The most obvious signature of oceanicity is a relatively small mean annual temperature range. Also typical of oceanicity are high *humidity* and abundant *precipitation*.

e.g. the British Isles, whose climate is dominated by the Atlantic Ocean.

TIP Proximity to the ocean does not always create the extreme oceanicity of the British Isles. If prevailing winds are offshore, the influence of the ocean may be small. Equally, cold ocean currents may lower winter temperatures well below the average for the latitude.

ocean trench: narrow, deep depression on the ocean floor adjacent to a *subduction zone*.

Ocean trenches develop along destructive plate margins. They mark the zone where a plate is subducted into the *mantle*. As the subducting plate descends into the mantle, it buckles the overriding plate to form a trench.

e.g. the 11 km deep Marianas Trench in the western Pacific, formed where the Pacific plate passes beneath the Philippine plate.

open-casting: extraction of mineral ores and fossil fuels by *quarrying* rather than by deep mining.

Open-cast operations are cheaper than deep mining, but have harmful environmental effects. Open-casting destroys landscapes and *ecosystems*, and creates noise, dust and unsightly earth embankments. In the UK, full landscape restoration is undertaken once mining operations have ended.

e.g. the UK, where open-casting accounts for an increasing proportion of national coal production. Much of this production comes from coalfields such as Northumberland and Derbyshire, formerly dominated by deep mining.

optimiser: decision-maker who acts only to maximise profits or minimise costs.

The optimiser concept figures prominently in neo-classical economic models. The optimiser concept simplifies decision-making, taking no account of behavioural, social, cultural, psychological factors etc.

e.g. decision-making in *Weber's theory* of industrial location, where industrialists choose sites that minimise total transport costs.

TIP Optimising behaviour is an unrealistic view of decision-making. In reality, decision-makers are *satisficers*, often motivated by non-economic goals and influenced by a variety of social, cultural and psychological factors.

optimum population: number of people in an area that can be sustained by existing technology and resource development at the highest standard of living.

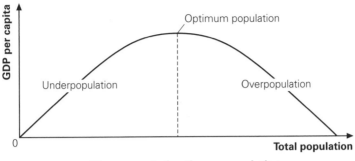

The concept of optimum population

In practice, it is almost impossible to define an optimum population. Resources vary with technology and rarely is the resource base of an area fully explored. Moreover, constant economic change means that the optimum population is unlikely to remain the same for any significant time.

TIP Optimum population is usually discussed in relation to natural resources. However, it can be considered in other contexts (e.g. the optimum size of a city for the provision of employment and services, or the optimum carrying capacity of grassland that maximises profits to farmers and is ecologically sustainable).

organic farming: type of farming that avoids the use of inorganic chemical fertilisers, herbicides or pesticides.

orogenesis: formation of mountain belts that have a linear planform.

e.g. orogenesis in the early Tertiary era, which produced the Himalayas, Andes, Alps and Rockies.

orographic precipitation: precipitation caused by the uplift of air as it crosses a hill or mountain barrier.

The orographic effect results in higher levels of mean annual precipitation in hilly and mountainous areas compared with adjacent lowlands. Often airmasses that are stable at lower altitudes become unstable as they ascend hills and mountains. This is known as conditional *instability*.

e.g. The highest mean annual precipitation totals in the British Isles (in excess of 5,000 mm a year) are found in mountainous areas such as the northwest Highlands, the Grampians and the Lake District.

out-migration: see *immigration*.

outwash: stratified sands and gravels deposited by meltwater streams and rivers.

Outwash forms a number of distinctive *glacio-fluvial* features such as *eskers*, *kames* and *sandar*.

overbank deposits: suspended sediment load of a river, deposited across the valley floor when a river floods.

Overbank deposits contribute to the alluvial fill of *flood plains*. In the British Isles, the sequence of flood plain deposits is often topped off with a layer of fine silt derived from overbank sediment.

■ *TIP* Remember that, in addition to overbank deposits that result from flooding, flood plains also comprise coarser channel deposits (i.e. former channel bars and *point bars*).

overflow channel: channel carved by meltwater either sub-glacially or through the overflow of a proglacial or marginal lake.

■ Overspill channels often have the dimensions of river valleys. However, unlike river valleys, they are frequently straight, steep-sided and semi-circular in cross-section.

■ *e.g.* Newtondale, North York Moors, formed by the overspill of water from ice-dammed lakes in the Esk Valley, southwards towards the Vale of Pickering.

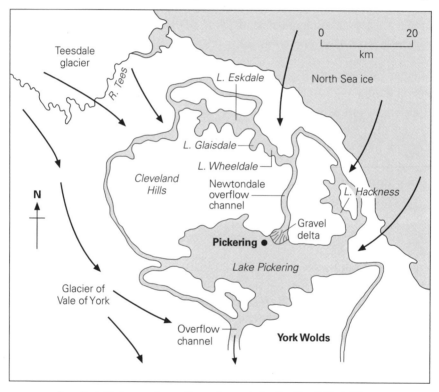

Proglacial lakes and overflow channels in the North York Moors

overgrazing: decline in the quality of pasture caused by overstocking.

■ Sustainable grazing is possible as long as livestock numbers do not exceed an area's *carrying capacity*. Population pressure, livestock subsidies and misman-agement may lead to overstocking. The first signs of overgrazing are a decrease in the more pallatable species. Extreme overgrazing destroys the vegetation cover and leads to accelerated *soil erosion*.

■ *e.g.* Britain's uplands have been overgrazed for centuries. The result is an absence of trees, a monoculture of grass and invasion by bracken. *Gullies* and soil erosion occur in the most overgrazed areas.

overland flow: movement of water as a thin film across the ground surface.

■ Overland flow occurs in two situations: (a) when the intensity of *precipitation* exceeds the soil's *infiltration capacity* (Hortonian overland flow); (b) when the water table reaches the ground surface (saturated overland flow).

■ *TIP* Overland flow is not the same as channel flow. The latter occurs when surface water flows in rivers, streams and *gullies*.

overpopulation: situation where a reduction in the population of an area would improve the population/resource ratio and standards of living.

■ Overpopulation is a relative concept that depends on resource availability, technology, world prices etc. Like *optimum population*, it is an elusive concept that may change over time.

■ *e.g.* the delta region of Bangladesh. This region supports the highest rural population densities in the world; farms are tiny, a large proportion of the population is landless and the people are poor and suffer frequent natural disasters such as tidal surges and river floods. Famines have occurred on several occasions in the last 100 years. Although not all experts would agree, there is a strong case for suggesting that Bangladesh's delta region is overpopulated.

■ *TIP* High population density is not the same as overpopulation. Some of the richest countries in the world (e.g. Japan, Netherlands, Belgium) support very high population densities.

overspill population: excess population in a town or city that cannot be housed within the existing urban area and is relocated in satellite towns in the surrounding region.

■ *e.g.* In the 1960s, Birmingham's overspill population was accommodated in New Towns such as Redditch and Telford and expanded towns such as Tamworth and Droitwich.

oxbow lake: abandoned or cut-off *meander* formed when a river straightens its course.

■ Oxbow lakes form when lateral *erosion* breaches the narrow neck of a meander and straightens the river's channel. The former meander is abandoned and eventually is infilled by *overbank deposits* and plant debris.

oxidation: absorption of oxygen by minerals either from the atmosphere or from water.

■ Oxidation is an important *chemical weathering* process. Oxidised minerals increase in volume, weakening rocks and causing their breakdown.

■ *TIP* Oxidation, together with *hydrolysis*, *hydration* and *solution*, is one the four most important chemical weathering processes.

ozone depletion: see *chlorofluorocarbons*.

pahoehoe: *basalt* lava with a smooth or ropy surface.

parallel drainage: drainage pattern where the main channels are regularly spaced and parallel to each other.

▨ Parallel drainage patterns are controlled by faulted and folded structures.

parallel retreat: slope retreat by *weathering*, *mass movement* and *erosion* which maintains both the angle and height of the slope profile (see *inselberg*).

▨ Parallel retreat is found in many arid and semi-arid environments. As the slope units retreat, they leave an extended, gently angled rock *pediment*.

▨ *e.g.* the mesa and buttes of Monument Valley, Utah, all of which have the same slope profiles.

▨ *TIP* Coastal cliffs, undercut by wave action, also show *parallel retreat*. The removal of eroded debris from the base of the cliff by waves ensures that cliffs maintain their profile.

parent material: rock that on *weathering* provides the mineral body of the soil.

▨ Parent material influences both the physical properties (e.g. texture, depth, colour, drainage) and the chemical properties (e.g. nutrient status, cation exchange capacity, acidity) of soils. Occasionally it is the dominant soil-forming factor (e.g. *intrazonal soils* such as rendzina on limestones).

▨ *TIP* Not all parent material is solid rock. In the British Isles, many soils have developed on glacial deposits such as sands and gravels and *boulder clay*.

patterned ground: polygons, nets, stripes and circles of stones in *periglacial environments*.

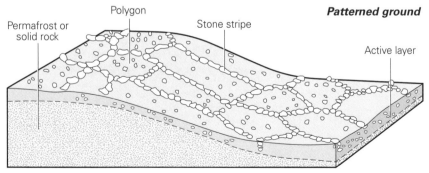

Patterned ground

■ Patterned ground may be sorted or unsorted (by size of stones). The development of patterned ground is associated with cracking (either by frost or by desiccation) of the *regolith* or *frost heave*. On steeper slopes, polygons and circles are replaced by stripes and nets.

ped: particles of sand, silt or clay that aggregate to form larger units.

■ Peds are responsible for the soil's structure. They allow water, air and plant roots to penetrate the soil and contribute significantly to soil fertility.

pediment: extensive shallow-angled rock platform that develops as a result of the parallel slope retreat (see *inselberg*).

■ Pediments dominate slopes in arid and semi-arid environments.

pedogenesis: formation of soil through the interaction of climate, *parent material,* vegetation, slopes and time.

■ The importance of each pedogenic factor varies geographically. It is generally assumed that, at the global and continental scales, climate is the dominant factor. However, at a local scale, where climate is often uniform, parent material and drainage are often responsible for differences in soil types. Soils take thousands of years to develop and in many environments (e.g. *salt marshes,* lava flows, recently *deglaciated* areas) soils may be immature.

■ *TIP* You should be able to assess the relative contribution of each soil-forming factor to pedogenesis, and provide examples of soil types dominated by each of the different factors.

peneplain: landscape of subdued relief, close to base level, formed by millions of years of *erosion*.

■ A peneplain is the final stage in the Davisian cycle of erosion. Such a feature can form only where the Earth's crust has remained stable for immense periods of time.

■ *e.g.* The world's shield areas (or *cratons*), such as the Baltic Shield and the Laurentian Shield, correspond most closely to the Davisian concept of peneplains.

perception: psychological function that enables an individual to convert sensory information into organised and coherent experience.

■ Perception is the way in which people build up an image of their environment. It is a subjective and selective process that is influenced by education, culture, age, experience and so on. There is often a considerable difference between an individual's perception of the environment and objective reality.

■ *e.g.* People's perceptions of natural hazards such as floods and droughts often underestimate risks, leaving them susceptible to disaster.

■ *TIP* To investigate human behaviour we need to know what people think. This means understanding their perception and images of the world.

periglacial environment: high-latitude and high-altitude regions not covered by *glaciers*, where temperatures are so low that the ground is permanently frozen.

■ Processes that operate with particular intensity in periglacial environments include *frost weathering, frost heave* and *gelifluction*. Typical periglacial landforms are *patterned ground, pingos*, gelifluction sheets/lobes/terraces, *screes* and *blockfields*.

■ *e.g.* the Yukon and Northwest Territories of Canada.

■ *TIP* Many periglacial processes and their associated landforms are found in the British Isles. Some processes (e.g. *frost weathering, solifluction*) are still active in upland areas today. Southern Britain (which was ice-free) was subject to intense periglacial activity during the last *glacial*. Relict periglacial landforms such as ognips (collapsed pingos), blockstreams and *head* are widespread.

periphery: areas that are geographically remote from a central *core* region and/or less prosperous than the core (see *Friedmann's core–periphery model*).

■ The periphery may be defined at global, continental or national scales. At a national scale, government *regional policies* aim to reduce the economic disparities between core and periphery. Peripheral regions often suffer structural unemployment, net migrational losses, low rates of economic growth, etc.

■ *e.g.* southern Italy, which occupies a peripheral location both within Italy and within the EU.

■ *TIP* The term 'periphery' is often used in an economic as well as a geographical sense. A region such as Nord-Pas-de-Calais is part of the EU's economic periphery, even though it lies within the EU's geographical core (i.e. the triangle approximated by London, Hamburg and Milan).

permafrost: permanently frozen ground in *periglacial environments*.

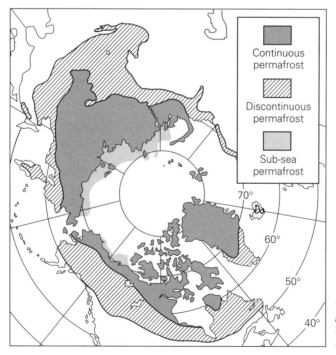

The distribution of the main permafrost types in the northern hemisphere

■ In high-latitude periglacial environments, the soil and regolith may be permanently frozen to a depth of several hundred metres. Only the surface metre or so — the active layer — of the permafrost melts during the summer months. Processes such as *frost weathering*, *frost heave* and *gelifluction* are concentrated in the active layer.

permeable rock: rock through which water can penetrate.

▨ Permeable rocks may have primary or secondary permeability. Rocks with primary permeability have pores (air spaces) between their mineral particles that can absorb water. These rocks are porous. Water penetrates rocks with secondary permeability through *joints* and bedding planes.

▨ *e.g.* Chalk has primary permeability; Carboniferous limestone has secondary permeability.

▨ *TIP* 'Permeable' is not the same as 'porous'. Although all porous rocks are permeable, not all permeable rocks are porous.

photosynthesis: process by which green plants convert water and carbon dioxide into starch and sugar in the presence of sunlight.

▨ Photosynthesis is the start of the *food chain*. Photosynthesising plants (autotrophs) fix the energy of sunlight through chlorophyll in their leaves. This energy is then passed along the food chain through herbivores, carnivores and detritivores (see *net primary productivity*).

phreatic cave: rounded tube-like cave in *karst* areas which forms below the *water table* (see *vadose cave*).

▨ Because phreatic caves develop below the water table, their floors, sides and roofs are equally eroded.

physical weathering (also called 'mechanical weathering')**:** in situ breakdown of rocks through temperature and moisture changes, without any alteration of their chemical composition.

▨ Physical weathering includes *frost weathering* (freeze–thaw), *salt weathering*, *insolation* weathering and *hydration*. The effect of physical weathering is to break up rocks into smaller particles. Landforms that result from physical weathering include *scree* or talus slopes and *blockfields*.

▨ *e.g.* the breakdown of granite by frost weathering on the Cairngorm Plateau into granular-sized particles.

▨ *TIP* The importance of physical weathering is that it provides rock particles (i.e. the tools) used by rivers, glaciers, waves and the wind for *erosion*.

pingo: small ice-cored, circular mound or small hill in *periglacial environments*.

▨ Pingos result from the segregation of ice in lenses (see *ice lens*) in the *permafrost*. The growth and concentration of this ground ice pushes the overlying *regolith* into a roughly symmetrical mound. When the ice core melts, it leaves a surface depression with circular ramparts known as an 'ognip'.

▨ *e.g.* Many pingos occur in the Mackenzie Delta in northern Canada.

pioneer community: first plants to colonise an environment during the process of *plant succession*.

▨ Pioneer species are usually herbs. In primary succession, these species are able to tolerate harsh environments (e.g. sand, bare rock, waterlogged areas) that exclude most other species.

■ *e.g.* Pioneer plants found in areas exposed by retreating *glaciers* in Canada include mountain avens, yellow saxifrage and arctic river beauty.

plagioclimax: stable vegetation community in equilibrium with environmental conditions and human activity.

■ In plagioclimax communities, human activities have arrested the normal succession.

■ *e.g.* Heather moorland in upland Britain is a plagioclimax community. It is maintained and managed for grouse-shooting by periodic firing. Firing encourages the growth of new heather shoots, which are the staple food of red grouse.

■ *TIP* You should be aware of the difference between *sub-climax* and plagioclimax vegetation. In a sub-climax, the arresting factor is natural (e.g. waterlogged soils).

plantation agriculture: type of agriculture found in tropical and sub-tropical environments which specialises in the production of just one or two cash crops for export.

■ Plantation agriculture is capital intensive and is often financed by *foreign direct investment* from *transnational corporations*.

■ *e.g.* banana plantations owned and operated by US companies in Central American countries such as Costa Rica and Guatemala.

plant succession: plant succession describes the change in the composition of vegetation at a given location through time.

■ Plant succession follows a sequence of stages, each with a distinctive plant community. These stages are known as *seres*. During the earlier stages of succession, there is usually an increase in *biodiversity, net primary production* and *biomass*. The final stage, which is in equilibrium with environmental conditions, is the *climax* community. There are two types of plant succession: primary succession and secondary succession. Primary succession occurs on newly exposed land (e.g. dunes, lava flows, mudflats). Secondary succession involves the redevelopment of vegetation on land that supported a vegetation cover in the past (e.g. derelict urban land).

■ *e.g.* Primary successions include *psammoseres* (sand dunes), *haloseres* (salt marsh), *lithoseres* (bare rock surfaces) and *hydroseres* (lakes, ponds, etc.).

■ *TIP* It is often helpful to view plant succession as a type of *positive feedback*. Earlier seral communities modify the environment (e.g. more soil, more shelter), which allows less tolerant species to invade and succeed. This process of modification and change in plant communities continues until the *climax* stage is reached.

plate tectonics: theory that the Earth's crust and *lithosphere* comprise a series of tectonic plates, and that the movement of these plates explains the distribution of volcanic activity, *earthquakes* and their associated landforms.

■ Plate tectonics, developed in the early 1960s, revolutionised earth science. It provided a unifying theory that explained *continental drift*, volcanic and earthquake activity, and landforms such as *island arcs*, fold mountain chains and *ocean trenches*. The key to the theory of plate tectonics was the discovery of *seafloor spreading*.

playa: basin-like area of inland drainage in a dryland region where salt deposits accumulate and which supports shallow lakes after *precipitation*.

plucking: see *quarrying*.

podzol: acidic, leached *zonal soil* that develops in association with the boreal coniferous forest.

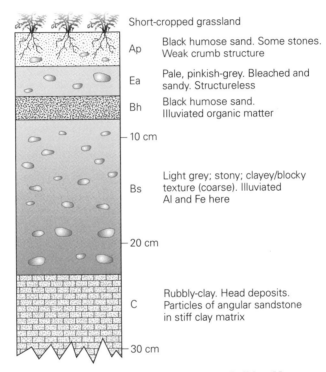

Podzol soil — well drained slope of 5–6°, Baildon Moor, West Yorkshire, 250 m above sea level

▨ Podzol soils develop in cold humid environments, where *precipitation* exceeds *evapotranspiration*. Rainwater infiltrating the soil removes nutrients by *leaching*, causes the breakdown of the clay–humus complex, and *eluviation* removes solid mineral and humus particles. The result is an extremely acidic soil and an eluviated horizon (Ea) of almost pure sand. Acidity is aggravated by the input of acidic mor litter from conifer needles. Podzol soils are sharply horizonated. The B horizon is one of *illuviation* where iron and aluminium oxides are washed in from above. In some podzols, a cemented layer of iron oxide (Bfe) develops and may impede soil drainage. The processes leading to the formation of podzol soils are known as 'podzolisation'.

▨ *e.g.* the soils that develop on glacial sands and gravels, beneath coniferous forest, in northern Sweden.

point bar: triangular-shaped area of coarse river sediment located opposite the undercut bank on a *meander*.

■ Point bars comprise coarse sediments, deposited at high flow on the inside of meandering river channels, where velocity is lowest. A current close to the river bed, from the outer to the inner bank, transfers sediment which builds up the point bar (see *helical flow*). Point bars are 'within channel' deposits and therefore an important source of *alluvium* for *flood plains*.

pools and riffles: alternating deeps and shallows in the long profiles of rivers.

■ At low discharges, velocity is faster over riffles than over pools. Gradients are steeper in riffle sections and the *bedload* is coarser. The characteristic flow in riffles is *turbulent*, compared to *laminar flow* in pools. However, pools and riffles develop at high discharges, when the velocity profiles are reversed. Frictional resistance between the water and the channel bed and banks sets up a pattern of alternating faster and slower flow. Faster flow in the pools causes *erosion* and transports coarser particles to the slower-flow riffle sections. Here *aggradation* occurs. The spacing of pools and riffles is approximately six times the channel width.

■ *TIP* You should be aware of the link between the spacing of pools and riffles and *meander* development. Pools (areas of fast flow and erosion) are found close to the outer bank in meandering channels, with riffles occupying the points of inflexion (see *meander*).

population: term used in statistics to describe the entire set of data from which a sample is drawn.

■ Populations in geography are usually very large. Most geographical investigations are based on a subset of the population (i.e. a sample).

■ *e.g.* all of the particles that make up a *scree slope*.

■ *TIP* There is a close relationship between the population and a sample. Sampling aims to produce an accurate subset of values that reflects the characteristics of the population.

population density: ratio of people to unit area.

■ Crude population density is the average number of people per square kilometre or per hectare. Residential density relates population to the size of the residential area and is a more sensitive indicator of overcrowding and social conditions. Even more sensitive is the average number of persons per room.

■ *e.g.* Egypt's crude population density is a moderate 63 persons per square kilometre. However, this figure masks the huge pressure of population on resources and the fact that 95% of the country is *desert*. A more accurate picture of population pressure is given by the number of persons per square kilometre of arable land, which in 1998 was 3,150.

■ *TIP* You should understand the shortcomings of crude population density as an indicator of overcrowding and the pressure of population on resources.

population momentum: potential for future growth in a population that has a large proportion of children.

A population with a large proportion of children is likely to experience significant growth in future. Within 10 to 20 years these children will be young adults and many will have children of their own, leading to further rapid population growth.

e.g. In Kenya 50% of the population is aged 15 years and under. The momentum of such a youthful population would normally lead to rapid population growth in future.

population policies: government policies designed to influence rates of *natural population change* and *net migrational change*.

Policies that promote population growth through higher fertility are pro-natalist. Those that encourage slower population growth through lower fertility are anti-natalist. Population policies can also be either pro or anti-*immigration*. The motives behind population policies are most often economic, but can also be political and social.

e.g. China's anti-natalist population policy is a response to perceived over-population in the 1970s. Without population control China's economic development would have been jeopardised.

TIP Population policies have both positive and negative effects. A strict anti-natalist policy will eventually reduce the number of young adults in the population. This may increase dependency and the burden of supporting an ageing population.

population pyramid: type of horizontal bar chart that shows the age–sex structure of a population in 1-year, 5-year or 10-year age groups.

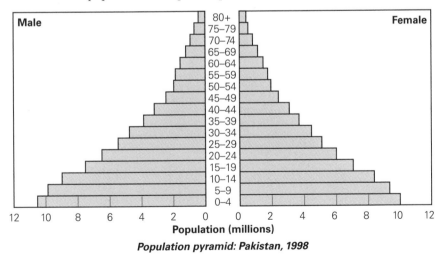

Population pyramid: Pakistan, 1998

The shape of a population pyramid reflects the influence of births, deaths and *migration* over a period of 80 or 90 years. Populations with high *fertility* and low *mortality* have broad-based, sharply tapering pyramids. Those with low fertility and low mortality are usually narrow at the base, straight-sided, and taper gradually towards the apex.

TIP The influence of migration on the shape of a population pyramid varies with scale. At the national scale, fertility and mortality dominate. However, at the local scale, migration often creates huge imbalances in age and gender.

positive correlation: see *correlation*.

positive feedback: relationship in a system where an initial change is amplified and leads to further change.

e.g. the growth of *ice sheets* during a *glacial*. The initial development of glaciers changes the *albedo* of the land surface. This causes more solar energy to be reflected back to space, which lowers temperatures and leads to further accumulations of ice. Change continues in the same direction until the Earth is plunged into a full-scale glacial.

positive skew: see *skewed frequency distribution*.

post-industrial economy: economy of an MEDC that in terms of employment and output is dominated by service activities.

In the last 200 years, the economies of today's MEDCs have moved through pre-industrial and industrial stages, to the current post-industrial stage.

e.g. The contribution made by financial services to output in the UK economy in 2000 exceeded the contribution of manufacturing industry.

TIP Keep a lookout for articles in newspapers and magazines about the increasing shift of employment from manufacturing to services. For instance, in May 2000, factory closures led to 1,500 job losses in the clothing industry in northeast England. But in the same month, a similar number of new jobs was created in call centres in the region.

pothole: circular hole in bedrock in a river channel formed by the abrasive action of rock particles caught up in vortices in turbulent river flow.

The effect of potholes is gradually to lower the bed of a river flowing in a solid rock channel.

TIP The term 'pothole' can also be used to describe *dolines* and caves in *karst* regions.

precipitation: water and ice that fall from clouds towards the Earth's surface.

The most common forms of precipitation are rain, drizzle, snow, sleet and hail. Precipitation occurs when droplets of water or particles of ice within clouds reach a critical size which the density of the atmosphere and updraughts of air can no longer support. The development of rain droplets in clouds is due to one of two processes: (a) collision between particles of moisture; (b) in clouds above the freezing level, the growth of ice particles by deposition.

TIP The droplets of water (and ice) that form clouds are tiny compared to rain droplets. To appreciate how rain and other types of precipitation form, we must understand the mechanisms by which these tiny cloud particles grow into much larger rain droplets.

pressure gradient: difference in pressure between two locations within the atmosphere or at the Earth's surface.

Pressure gradient is the master force that drives the wind. Wind speed is directly proportional to the pressure gradient. A steep pressure gradient describes a large pressure difference over a relatively short distance. On weather charts, steep pressure gradients (and strong winds) are shown by *isobars* closely packed together. A slack pressure gradient occurs when spatial differences in pressure are small and isobars are widely spaced. Slack pressure gradients generate only light winds.

▧ *TIP* If the pressure gradient were the only force acting on the wind, winds would blow directly from high to low pressure. In reality, winds blow almost parallel to isobars. This tells us that a second force — the *Coriolis force* — balances the pressure gradient force.

pressure release (also called 'dilatation'): expansion of rocks following unloading, which leads to the formation of *joints* aligned parallel to the ground surface.

▧ Unloading occurs through the removal of overlying rocks by *erosion* and by the melting of *ice sheets* during *deglaciation*. This resultant expansion causes cracking parallel to the surface, and the formation of joints or pseudo-bedding planes.

▧ *e.g.* the horizontal joint structures in granite *tors*.

▧ *TIP* Pressure release is responsible for *sheeting* in granitic rocks.

prevailing wind: wind direction that occurs most often at a place.

▧ The direction of the prevailing wind has important implications for climate. For instance, onshore winds bring humid airmasses and the temperature characteristics of the surrounding seas and oceans. In contrast, offshore winds are associated with drier airmasses and continental conditions.

▧ *e.g.* The prevailing westerly winds are largely responsible for the extreme *oceanicity* of the British Isles' climate.

primacy: situation where the largest city in a country is more than twice the size of the second city.

▧ A primate city dominates the urban hierarchy of a country. Urban primacy is found in: LEDCs where the urban hierarchy was established under colonialism; countries with highly centralised governments; countries that in the eighteenth and nineteenth centuries controlled large empires; and small countries where there is little need for a second tier of cities.

▧ *e.g.* Buenos Aires, Argentina's primate city. Buenos Aires has a population more than ten times larger than the second city, Cordoba.

▧ *TIP* Compare urban primacy with the *rank-size distribution*.

primary sector: economic activities that produce food, fuel and raw materials.

▧ The primary sector covers industries such as agriculture, mining, quarrying, fisheries, forestry and water supplies. The products of the primary sector are unprocessed and have little added value. Agriculture is the leading primary activity, employing nearly one in two of the world's workforce.

primary succession: see *plant succession*.

prisere: entire sequence of communities in a plant succession, from initial colonisers to *climax vegetation*.

e.g. In a recently *deglaciated* valley in Alberta, a typical prisere might include: (1) lichens and mosses; (2) herbaceous plants (e.g. saxifrages, mountain avens); (3) shrubs and bushes (e.g. dwarf willow, dwarf birch); (4) small trees (e.g. silver birch, aspen); (5) climax forest of Douglas fir.

producer service (also called 'quaternary activities'): activities such as finance, trade, research and development, advertising and consultancy that provide services to other economic activities.

product life cycle: sequence of stages in the production of a manufactured item from development, through maturity to standardisation.

The significance of the product life cycle for geography is that products, at different stages of the cycle, have different locational requirements. In the early development stage, skilled labour is needed (e.g. technicians, scientists) and production locates near to research and development and company head-quarters (often in the *core*). When the product is perfected (i.e. at maturity), production is decentralised away from the core. With standardisation, *mass production* begins. There is a demand for cheaper, unskilled labour. Thus locations in the *periphery* are increasingly favoured.

TIP You may be able to get more out of the product life cycle theory in a written examination question if you appreciate that the theory can be applied at different scales. For instance, the core area — the preferred location in the development stage — may be a large metropolitan region in a MEDC or, at a global scale, all MEDCs. In the later stages of the cycle, peripheral locations may be interpreted as relatively poor or geographically isolated regions in MEDCs or, globally, all LEDCs.

psammosere: *plant succession* that occurs on coastal *dunes*.

A psammosere is a type of *xerosere* where the main limiting factor in plant succession is lack of water.

e.g. In the British Isles, transects across dune complexes such as Ainsdale (Lancashire) show a zonation of species. Each zone represents a seral community in a psammosere (see *sere*).

push–pull factors: factors that (a) force migrants to leave their place of origin and (b) attract them to a new destination (see *Lee's migration model*).

Push factors are the negative attributes of a migrant's place of origin. They may include unemployment, poor service provision, wars and environmental disasters. Pull factors are the positive attributes of a place of destination. Many pull factors are simply the reverse of push factors, such as employment oppor-tunities and good-quality services. The most powerful push and pull factors are economic ones.

e.g. The *migration* of asylum seekers to the UK results from a combination of push and pull factors. Political persecution in the migrant's place of origin is the push factor. The pull of the UK might include its political stability, tolerance and tradition of accepting asylum seekers.

TIP Most migration movements result from both push and pull factors. These factors (especially the pull factors) are mediated through the migrants' own *perceptions*. The migrants' images of places of destination are often highly inaccurate. In part this explains why for every migration there is a complementary return migration.

pyroclastic flow: fast-moving, fluid-like flow of ash, larger rock fragments and hot gases caused by a violent volcanic eruption.

■ *e.g.* the eruption of Vesuvius in AD 79, when a pyroclastic flow overwhelmed the Roman town of Pompeii.

quarrying (also called 'plucking'): major glacial *erosion* process.

▓ Ice at the base of a *glacier* melts through pressure. Meltwater finds its way into rock joints where it refreezes. This freeze–thaw process weakens the rock. As ice flows over and adheres to the rock, fragments are removed.

▓ *e.g.* The steep downglacier side of a *roche moutonnée* results from glacial quarrying.

Quaternary era: last 2 million years of geological time, which includes the Pleistocene and Holocene periods.

quaternary sector: see *producer service*.

quinary sector: service activities that are consumer-oriented.

▓ The quinary sector provides services to individuals. It includes health services, education, government, entertainment, tourism, recreation and retailing.

▓ *TIP* Definitions of sub-divisions of the service sector are often inconsistent. A useful distinction is to think of the quinary sector as providing services to individuals, while the quaternary sector provides services to commercial organisations.

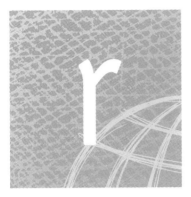

radiation fog: fog formed when the air is chilled by radiative cooling of the ground, usually at night (see *fog*).

raindrop impact: effect of raindrops hitting loose soil particles and dislodging them downslope.

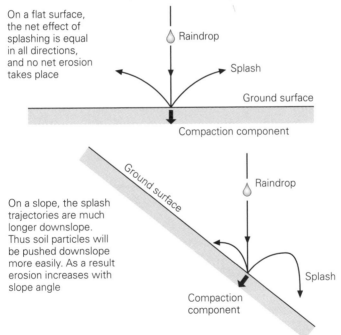

On a flat surface, the net effect of splashing is equal in all directions, and no net erosion takes place

Raindrop

Splash

Ground surface

Compaction component

Raindrop

On a slope, the splash trajectories are much longer downslope. Thus soil particles will be pushed downslope more easily. As a result erosion increases with slope angle

Ground surface

Splash

Compaction component

Raindrop impact

▓ Raindrop impact is a slope transport process. On a slope, the effect of gravity on rain splash will cause more particles to move downslope than upslope. The result is a net downslope displacement of soil particles.

▓ *TIP* Raindrop impact is only important as a slope transport process where slopes have little or no vegetation cover.

rain shadow: area of below average precipitation situated to the lee of a large upland.

■ Airmasses crossing high ground will shed much of their moisture on the windward slope and summital area. Humidity also falls because air descending the leeward slope warms adiabatically, thus further reducing the likelihood of *precipitation*.

■ *e.g.* The rain shadow created by the Himalaya and Tibet Plateau is responsible for the extreme aridity of the Gobi Desert in central Asia.

raised beach: former shorelines up to 45 m above current sea level, comprising beach deposits and *shore platforms*, and in some cases backed by relict cliffs.

■ Raised beaches are the result of isostatic recovery (see *glacio-isostacy*) following *deglaciation*. In northern Britain in the past 10,000 years, the rate of isostatic uplift has exceeded the rate of eustatic sea level rise.

■ *e.g.* The best-developed raised beaches in the British Isles are found in northwest Scotland. There the Devensian ice was thickest and thus isostatic recovery has been greater than elsewhere. A prominent raised beach exists at 8 m above OD around the northwest coast.

■ *TIP* On a few coastlines in the British Isles (e.g. south Devon), ancient beaches (mainly rocky shore platforms) survive from the last *inter-glacial*. Although now above sea level, these beaches were cut when sea level was 8–10 m higher than today. Unlike raised beaches, they are not related to isostatic change.

random sampling: scientific procedure for selecting samples where every individual or item in the *population* has an equal chance of selection.

■ The purpose of any sampling strategy is to obtain a sample that accurately represents the population. Random sampling, normally carried out by using random numbers, is one means of achieving this. Statistical methods for analysing samples are based on the assumption that sample data accurately represent the population.

■ *e.g.* using random numbers to select individual households from an electoral register.

■ *TIP* Many students forget that 'random' has a precise statistical meaning. It doesn't mean that individuals and items are included in a sample without conscious bias by the researcher. Random sampling means using random numbers.

range: maximum distance travelled to purchase a good or service (see *central place theory*).

■ The range of a good or service depends on its *threshold*. A good or service draws customers from its *trade area*. The higher the threshold, the bigger the trade area and the greater the range. The range of goods and services determines the spacing of settlements in central place theory.

■ *e.g.* Food is a convenience good that is purchased frequently and has a low threshold. This threshold can be met within a relatively small trade area. Hence the range of food is also small.

■ *TIP* The range of a good or service will also depend on local circumstances (e.g. population density, purchasing power of the population, transport).

rank-size distribution: urban hierarchy in a country where the largest city is twice as big as the second city, three times the size of the third city and so on.

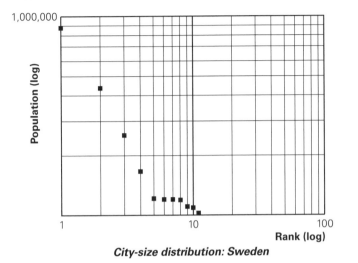

City-size distribution: Sweden

The rank-size rule states that a city's population is equal to:

$$p_i = p_1/i$$

where p_i is the population of the *i*th ranking town and p_1 is the population of the largest centre. For instance, if the largest city has a population of 1 million, the fifth largest city should have a population of 1,000,000/5 or 200,000.

e.g. the rank-size hierarchies of the USA and India.

TIP The opposite city-size distribution to rank-size is known as a primate distribution (see *primacy*). There is no single explanation for rank-size distributions. Although longer-established 'mature' settlement hierarchies are more likely to show rank-size tendencies, many European countries (e.g. UK, France, Denmark) have primate city-size distributions.

recumbent fold: type of fold where the strata are overturned and both limbs of the fold are almost horizontal (see *folding*).

Further pressure leads to shearing of the upper part of the fold along a thrust fault and the development of a *nappe*.

recurrence interval: frequency with which a stream discharge of given magnitude is likely to occur.

Recurrence intervals are used to calculate the likelihood of *bankfull* discharge and flood frequency, and have important implications for *flood plain* management. Many flood control structures such as *levées* are designed to give protection against flood events that might recur once or twice every century.

recurved lateral: hook-like shingle ridges that develop at the seaward end of *spits* (see *longshore drift*).

Recurved laterals are evidence of longshore drift. Beaches which show *drift alignment*, such as spits, grow laterally along the coastline by longshore drift.

The seaward (or distal) ends of spits often terminate in a hook-like recurve, formed by wave *refraction* around the end of the spit.

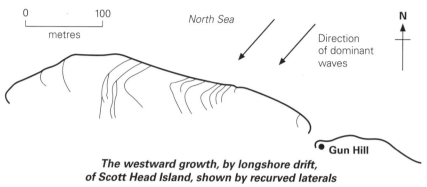

The westward growth, by longshore drift, of Scott Head Island, shown by recurved laterals

▨ *TIP* The absence of recurved laterals along a beach is strong evidence of *swash alignment,* suggesting it was not formed by the longshore movement of sediment.

refraction: bending of waves in the nearshore zone until they break almost parallel to the coast.

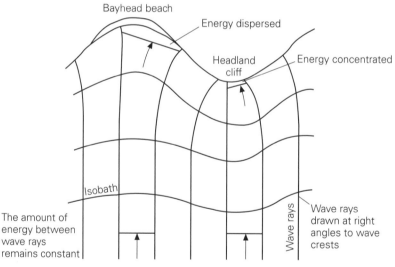

Wave refraction and the distribution of energy along coastlines

▨ Wave refraction is caused by the slowing of waves (due to friction) as they enter shallow water. When waves are fully refracted, the *swash* and *backwash* follow the same path up and down the beach. If this situation prevails, there is little or no *longshore drift* and beaches with *swash alignment* develop.

▨ *TIP* Refraction is also responsible for the uneven distribution of wave energy on coastlines. It concentrates energy on headlands and disperses it in bays. You should understand the implications of this for landform development on coasts.

regional policy: see *assisted area* and *Objective 1 and 2 areas.*

regional shopping centre: planned edge-of-town shopping centre, comparable in scale and range of shops to the central shopping area of a large town or city.

■ Regional shopping centres offer a full range of high street shops. They are dominated by *multiple retailers* and two or three major anchor tenants such as Marks and Spencer, Tesco and Boots. Most regional shopping centres are fully enclosed and support a wide range of product and service retailers. They provide extensive free parking and are 'event' places, with restaurants, fast-food outlets, cinemas, indoor theme parks etc. as well as shops.

■ *e.g.* the Trafford Centre, Manchester.

■ *TIP* Regional shopping centres are the ultimate example of the decentralisation of retailing. They are controversial because they often have an adverse effect on traditional shopping centres in surrounding towns and cities. For this reason, UK planners are unlikely to approve any new regional shopping centres in the near future. You should clarify your own views on the desirability of out-of-town shopping.

regolith: weathered rock debris and soil at the Earth's surface that mantles the unaltered solid rock.

■ The depth of regolith at any location often indicates the effectiveness of *weathering* and transport processes.

regression: statistical technique for fitting a trend line to data plotted on a scattergraph (see *correlation*).

■ Regression lines summarise the relationship between two (or more) variables. They also enable variable *y* to be predicted from variable *x*.

■ *e.g.* Stream discharge (*y*) could be regressed against drainage basin area (*x*) for a number of drainage basins in a region. From this simple model, it would be possible to predict the discharge of unmeasured streams from their basin areas.

■ *TIP* Relationships between variables are not always linear. Before fitting a regression line, you must check the pattern of points on a scattergraph. If the trend is curvilinear, you may have to transform the data using a logarithmic scale before attempting to fit a regression line.

Reilly's model: type of *gravity model* used to define the boundaries of *trade areas* around *central places*.

■ Reilly's model assumes that the extent and shape of a settlement's trade area is directly proportional to (a) its *centrality* and (b) the location of competing centres. As with other gravity models, a variety of measures can be used to represent centrality (e.g. population, employment, retail floor space, number of shops). To calculate the break-point of the trade boundary between settlements i and j, the following formula is used:

$$B_i = \frac{D_{ij}}{1 + \sqrt{P_i/P_j}}$$

where B_i = the location of the break-point between i and j
in terms of distance from i

D_{ij} = the distance between i and j

P_i = the population of i

P_j = the population of j

■ *TIP* To delimit the trade area using Reilly's model, you must draw boundaries from each break-point at right-angles to the lines which join the principal settlement to surrounding settlements. A common error is to join each break-point to its neighbour with a straight line to form a polygon.

rejuvenation: renewed energy of rivers resulting from a fall in *base level*, which causes incision.

■ A fall in base level increases a river's gradient and therefore its power. The response is renewed *erosion* and the development of landforms such as *rejuvenation terraces*, incised *meanders*, gorges and *knickpoints*.

■ *TIP* Changes other than a fall in base level can increase a river's power (e.g. increased discharge, climate change, *deglaciation*, tectonic uplift). These changes can also produce landforms similar to those caused by rejuvenation.

rejuvenation terraces: remnants of former *flood plain* surfaces, abandoned by a river that has incised its channel into the valley floor.

■ Unlike *meander terraces*, rejuvenation terraces are paired (at the same height) on opposite sides of the valley. This suggests that incision was rapid.

rendzina: type of *intrazonal soil* that owes its main characteristics to limestone *parent material*.

Rendzina soils, although often found in climatic environments where *leaching* is prevalent, have relatively high pH values (e.g. 7 or 8). This reflects the influence of a calcareous parent material such as chalk and limestone.

■ *TIP* Soils that develop on lime-rich parent materials are not always alkaline. Some limestones (e.g. Carboniferous limestone) are very hard and resist *weathering*. Thus in the limestone districts of the Pennines, the effect of leaching more than offsets the influence of the calcareous parent material and produces slightly acidic soils.

renewable resource: natural resource that is either inexhaustible or follows a biological or physical cycle of continuous renewal.

■ *e.g.* Solar energy is an inexhaustible resource; plant and animal resources (e.g. timber and fish) reproduce themselves over relatively short time scales; and water, through the *water cycle*, is continuously renewed.

retail park: planned out-of-town shopping area, dominated by several large retail sheds and with extensive on-site parking.

■ Retail parks specialise in high-order comparison goods, many of which have traditionally located in the *central business district* (CBD) (e.g. household electrical goods, DIY, furniture). Most units are single-storey, have a large floor space and are operated by *multiple retailers*. Retail park customers are usually one-stop shoppers who travel there by car. Unlike the central shopping area of the CBD and regional shopping centres, retail parks are not integrated shopping centres.

■ *e.g.* the Crown Point retail park in Leeds.

■ *TIP* You should be aware of the contrasts between the two main types of planned urban retail centre — retail parks and *regional shopping centres* (types of retail unit, shopping behaviour, access, travel patterns etc.).

reurbanisation: movement of people back to the inner areas of cities in MEDCs from the outer suburbs and *exurbs*.

■ Planners encourage reurbanisation as a means of revitalising the inner areas of cities, reducing the length of journeys to work and traffic congestion. In most British cities, few people live in the *central business district (CBD)*. Currently, efforts are being made to attract people to converted office buildings, converted warehouses, waterfront sites near canals and docks, redeveloped *brownfield sites* etc. in and around the CBD. The process of *gentrification* is part of this trend towards reurbanisation.

■ *e.g.* revitalised dockland and industrial sites such as the Eldonian village, Liverpool, on the site of the former Tate and Lyle sugar refinery.

reverse fault: upward displacement of strata along a fault line caused by compression in the Earth's crust (see *faulting*).

revetment: *hard engineering* coastal defence structure, designed to absorb wave energy and reduce *erosion*.

■ Revetments are fence-like, open wooden structures that absorb wave energy. Sediment accumulates on the landward side of revetments and provides further protection against erosion.

■ *TIP* You should appreciate the economic and environmental advantages and disadvantages of hard engineering coastal defensive structures designed to stop erosion. Such an evaluation should also take account of alternative soft engineering responses such as *beach nourishment* and *managed retreat*.

ria: incised river valley drowned by the post-glacial rise in sea level.

■ Rias develop on upland coastlines and are steep-sided, deep and branching.

■ *e.g.* valleys such as the River Dart and Kingsbridge Estuary in south Devon.

ribbon lake: long, narrow lake occupying the floor of a *glacial trough*.

■ Some ribbon lakes occupy depressions where intense glacial *erosion* has scoured the valley floor. Others have formed where recessional *moraines* have created a natural dam across the valley.

■ *e.g.* Wastwater, Cumbria.

ridge and runnel: shore-parallel ridges and troughs found on shallow sand beaches.

■ Ridges and runnels are features of the low-tide terrace on flat sand beaches. The ridges rarely exceed 1 m in height and are often as much as 100 m apart. The runnels are drained at low tide by transverse channels. Ridges and runnels are formed by wave action as the tide rises and falls. They may persist for several tidal cycles.

rift valley: alternative name for a *graben*.

river regime: average discharge of a river over an extended period of time.

The term is usually applied to average annual or monthly variations in discharge. In the British Isles, most rivers have their maximum discharge in winter when soils are saturated and *evapotranspiration* is low. A spring flow maximum is typical of rivers draining glacial and periglacial regions. In the seasonally humid tropics (e.g. monsoon Asia), the wet season is the period of high flow.

roche moutonnée: rock outcrop that has been abraded and quarried by glacial action.

Roches moutonnées have two contrasting slope forms. The slope that faced upglacier has been smoothed and lowered by glacial *abrasion*. In contrast, the downglacier slope has been quarried (see *quarrying*) and steepened.

TIP Roches moutonnées demonstrate at a small scale the relationship between geomorphological process and form.

Rostow model: five-stage model of economic development.

The model suggests that countries can be placed in one of five stages of economic development: traditional society, pre-conditions for 'take-off', the 'take-off' to self-sustained growth, the drive to maturity, and the age of mass consumption. These stages are sequential. The critical stage is 'take-off', marking the transition from an LEDC to an MEDC economy.

TIP In practice, it is very difficult to identify each development stage and especially the critical stage of 'take-off'.

rotational slide: downslope movement of rock and/or *regolith* as a coherent body, along a curved slide plane (see *landslide*).

runoff: movement of water across the land surface.

Runoff occurs as channel flow (rills, *gullies*, streams, rivers) and as *overland flow* (a thin film or sheet of water). Runoff is responsible for the stormflow or quickflow on a storm or flood *hydrograph*.

rural depopulation: absolute decline in the population in a rural area.

Depopulation normally results from a net migrational population loss rather than natural decrease. However, severe depopulation may be a combination of both. Depopulation has both demographic and economic effects. Because migration is a selective process, depopulated rural communities often have aged population structures and unbalanced *sex ratios*. In MEDCs the economic impact of depopulation often leads to declining service provision in rural areas (e.g. reduced public transport services, shop closure, closure of primary schools).

e.g. Rural depopulation has been a feature of some of the remotest areas of the UK for the past 150 years. These areas include the Western Isles, central Wales and the northern Pennines.

TIP Rural service decline in MEDCs is not confined to depopulated rural communities in remote areas. Many rural commuter belts around major cities and conurbations have also experienced service decline, but for different reasons.

rurality: degree to which an area can be defined as rural rather than urban.

- There is no simple definition of rural areas. Instead an index of rurality, based on land use, economic activities, population density and culture has been used to describe the extent to which an area is rural. Rural areas usually have the following characteristics: low-intensity land use (e.g. agriculture, forestry, recreation and leisure, water supply); resource-based economic activities (e.g. agriculture); low population densities; and traditional attitudes and lifestyles.

- *TIP* Although national censuses define rural (and urban) populations, the criteria used vary between countries. Thus any international comparisons of rural (and urban) populations should be treated with caution.

rural–urban fringe: zone of rural land use immediately adjacent to a large town or city.

- Rural land use in the fringe is strongly influenced by the proximity of the urban area. Typical fringe land uses that reflect the demands of urban dwellers include schools, sports grounds, crematoria, sewage treatment works and horse livery. Farmland may become derelict in anticipation of its conversion to urban use.

- *TIP* You should be able to describe and explain the differences between fringe land uses and those found in the 'deep' countryside.

salinisation: accumulation in the soil of salts that are toxic to plants, often to the point where agriculture cannot continue.

■ Salinisation is a widespread problem in many dryland areas where agriculture relies on *irrigation*. Over-irrigation causes a rise in the level of the *water table*, and high temperatures draw water to the surface by capillary action. Subsequent *evaporation* leads to the deposition of salts from *solution*. In extreme cases, a saline crust may develop, and cultivation may be abandoned.

■ *e.g.* Indus Valley, Pakistan.

■ *TIP* Salinisation is not just a problem in LEDCs. Many dryland areas in Australia and the USA have also been badly affected.

saltation: transport of sand grains by wind on *beaches*, coastal *dunes* and in *desert* environments.

■ Sand particles entrained by the wind move by skipping over the surface. As each particle hits the surface, it collides with other particles and sets them in motion. This movement is confined to within 1 m or so of the surface.

■ *TIP* Saltation also transports sand in stream and river channels.

salt marsh: vegetated *mudflats* situated above the mean high tide level (see *halosere*).

■ Salt marshes grow by the accretion of fine sediments, carried by tidal currents, in low-energy coastal environments such as *estuaries*. They are submerged only at the highest spring tides. Typical salt marsh plants, adapted to occasional inundation and salinity, are thrift, sea aster, sea lavender, sea arrow grass and sea purslane.

salt weathering: growth of salt crystals from *solution* in porous rocks, which sets up internal stress and causes disintegration.

sampling: see *random sampling, stratified sampling* and *systematic sampling*.

sandur (plural 'sandar'): extensive spread of sand and gravel deposited by meltwater in a lowland area (see *outwash*).

■ *e.g.* the Skeidarasandur in southeast Iceland formed by the deposition of sand and gravel by meltwater draining the Vatnajökull icefield.

satisficer: decision-maker who has bounded knowledge and limited ability to use it and who is often motivated by non-economic goals.

■ Satisficers approximate decision-makers in the real world. Decisions are made on the basis of incomplete knowledge, limited ability and imperfect *perception*. The idea of satisficing behaviour is a reaction to the unrealistic assumptions of optimising behaviour in classic economic models (see *optimiser*).

■ *e.g.* People moving house may search only a small part of the available housing market. They may settle for a satisfactory outcome that is convenient rather than optimal (the perfect house).

scarp slope: shorter, steeper slope on an *escarpment* or cuesta.

science park: purpose-built industrial areas, often located on edge-of-town sites and dedicated to research and development, and knowledge-based industries.

■ There are 50 science parks in the UK. They accommodate over 1,400 knowledge-based industries and employ around 25,000 people. Science parks are often dominated by small businesses and start-up companies that are spin-offs from large, successful firms. Many science parks have an 'incubator' function, nurturing the growth of new companies. They also have close ties with universities.

■ *e.g.* the Cambridge Science Park, established in 1972 and located on a *greenfield site* on the edge of town.

scree slope (also called 'talus slope'): concave debris slope beneath a cliff or free-face, comprising coarse rock particles.

■ Scree particles are derived from freeze–thaw weathering of the free-face and subsequent rockfall. Depending on the size of particles, a typical scree has an angle of between 30 and 40 degrees. Most screes in Britain's uplands are fossil features formed during periglacial conditions at the end of the Devensian *glacial*.

■ *e.g.* the Great Stone Chute in the Black Cuillin of Skye — the longest scree slope in the British Isles.

seafloor spreading: formation of new oceanic crust at a *mid-ocean ridge* and its slow lateral divergence away from the ridge.

■ Seafloor spreading starts when convection currents in the *mantle* bring *magma* to the surface and form new oceanic crust. Pressure from the new crust pushes the old crust sideways at a rate of 2–3 cm a year. This movement is the key to understanding *continental drift*. The whole cycle from the formation of new oceanic crust to its eventual destruction (in *subduction zones*) takes around 200 million years.

■ *TIP* The discovery of seafloor spreading in the early 1960s led to a revolution in earth sciences and the theory of *plate tectonics*.

sea wall: concrete wall built along a stretch of coastline and designed to stop marine *erosion* and *floods*.

■ Sea walls are rigid structures that reflect, rather than absorb, wave energy. Although they give complete protection against erosion, they are expensive to build and require constant maintenance.

■ *TIP* Be aware of the advantages and disadvantages of sea walls and their *sustainability* in view of the projected rises in sea level in the next 50 years.

secondary sector: economic sector that covers manufacturing industries.

■ Manufacturing activities process raw materials, fabricate semi-finished products and assemble components. In doing so, they add value to materials, products and finished goods. In the UK around 16% of the workforce is engaged in the secondary sector — a proportion that has shrunk massively in the past 50 years and is still shrinking.

■ *e.g.* oil refining (processing industry); steel shaping (fabricating industry); aeroplanes (assembly industry).

■ *TIP* Although employment in the secondary sector in MEDCs in the past 50 years has declined, output has risen. This is because automation has created more efficient manufacturing systems.

secondary succession: see *plant succession*.

sediment cell: stretches of coastline that are self-contained cycles of *erosion* and sediment deposition.

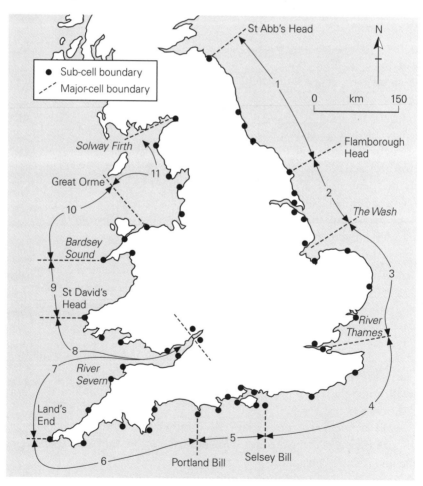

Coastal sediment cells in England and Wales

Sediment cells are closed systems. Sand and shingle are confined to each cell and there is little or no input of sediment from adjacent cells. Sediment cells are the basic unit of shoreline management in England and Wales.

e.g. The coastline of England and Wales is divided into 11 major sediment cells.

TIP Think of the implications of removing sediments (e.g. for aggregates for construction) from a stretch of coastline. How do sediment cells compare with river basins as natural units for environmental management?

segregation: geographical separation of social, economic and ethnic groups within large urban areas.

Segregation by income occurs because higher-income groups can afford to purchase housing and land in the more desirable suburbs. Deliberate distancing by some social groups from perceived inferior social groups also explains segregation. The degree of segregation along ethnic lines depends on the cultural distance between minority groups and the majority. The greater the differences, the more segregated the ethnic group. Extreme segregation gives rise to *ghettos*.

e.g. the concentration of many Muslim communities in the inner suburbs of UK cities.

TIP Remember that segregation can be either forced or voluntary. Prejudice and discrimination often lead to the forced segregation of ethnic minority groups. However, segregation is also a way for these groups to retain their traditions and sense of community.

sere: stage of ecological succession with a distinctive assemblage of plant species.

Seres are temporary stages in the succession of plants to *climax*. Seral communities modify soil, light, shelter and hydrological conditions, which allows the invasion of new species.

e.g. alder carr is a stage in ecological succession and is therefore a sere.

TIP You should consider why successive seres are normally more *biodiverse* and productive and have a greater *biomass* than those they displace. You should also apply the systems concepts of *positive feedback* and equilibrium to seres.

service sector: see *tertiary, quaternary, quinary sectors* and *producer services*.

sex ratio: proportion of females to males in a population, usually expressed as the number of females per 1,000 males.

In human populations at the national scale, females normally outnumber males. This is because females have longer *life expectancies*. Thus the imbalance in sex ratios is apparent only in older age groups. At more local scales, imbalances in sex ratios are usually due to the selective effects of *migration*.

e.g. In sub-Saharan Africa, males are more likely to migrate than females. As a result, males often heavily outnumber females in towns and cities. In South America, this pattern is reversed.

TIP You should be aware of the social, economic and demographic consequences of major imbalances between males and females in a population.

shake hole: small funnel-shaped subsidence *doline*.

shanty town: unplanned and spontaneous illegal settlement in a city in a LEDC.

■ Shanty towns are found throughout the economically developing world. They are known as favelas in Brazil, colonias in Mexico, bustees in India, etc. The massive growth of illegal and unplanned settlements (which may form up to 50% of the housing in some cities) reflects (a) the scale and speed of current urbanisation and (b) the inability of urban authorities to provide sufficient low-cost housing for the people.

■ *e.g.* Kibera in Nairobi, Kenya, which is Africa's largest shanty town.

■ *TIP* Shanty towns should be viewed positively, as an example of enterprise and self-help by the poor. Once upgraded, shanty towns become part of the suburbs. You should note that many poor urban dwellers live in shanty towns out of choice. Housing in shanty towns is free, and many shanty towns are conveniently located close to sources of casual employment (e.g. factories, docks, *central business district*).

sheeting: removal of rock in thick sheets or layers owing to *pressure release*.

■ Sheeting is most common in granite and occurs when unloading causes the rock to expand parallel to the surface. Sheeting can give rise to *exfoliation domes*.

shifting cultivation: traditional method of cultivation in tropical rainforest environments, whose main feature is the rotation of land rather than the rotation of crops.

■ Shifting cultivation is a sustainable system of farming in environments where soils are too poor to support permanent cultivation. Farmers clear small plots of rainforest, burn the branches and foliage (which fertilises the soil and kills weeds) and cultivate the land for one or two years. As soil fertility and yields decline, farmers abandon the plot, clear a new area of forest and initiate a new cycle of cultivation.

■ *TIP* Shifting cultivation is a sustainable system as long as farmers allow the abandoned plots to recover their fertility. Normally this takes at least 25 years. Shifting cultivation is threatened where population growth shortens the fallow period.

shoreline management plans (SMPs): strategies developed by local authorities and the Environmental Agency in England and Wales to coordinate planning of the coastline.

■ SMPs are being developed for each *sediment cell* in England and Wales. They are an attempt to view stretches of coastline with discrete sediment budgets as single units. Because changes in one part of a sediment cell are likely to have knock-on effects elsewhere, it makes sense to coordinate planning between the various bodies responsible for the coastline.

shore platform (also called 'wave-cut platform'): extensive solid rock platform on upland coastlines which slopes gently seawards.

■ Shore platforms result from cliff retreat caused by marine *erosion*. But in addition to the abrasive and quarrying effects of wave action, *sub-aerial processes* such as *weathering* (biological, physical and chemical) contribute to shore platform development. There is some debate concerning the ages of shore platforms. Some may have developed in the last 6,000 years. Others are so large that they must have formed during previous *inter-glacials* when sea level was similar to today's.

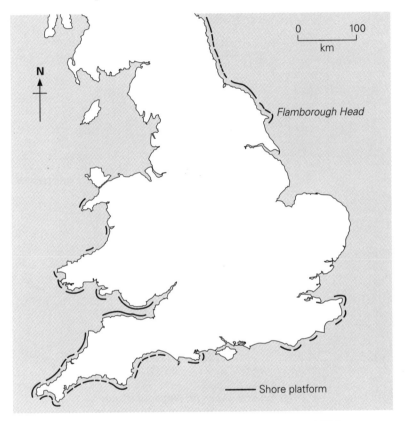

The distribution of shore platforms in England and Wales

- **e.g.** the shore platform at Selwick's Bay, Flamborough Head, cut in resistant chalk.
- **TIP** Although still widely used, the term 'wave-cut platform' is inaccurate because it ignores the importance of sub-aerial processes.

sill: minor *igneous intrusion* comprising a horizontal sheet of *magma* that cooled within the crust.

- The magma that forms sills was injected between two layers of rock. Thus sills (in contrast to *dykes*) are concordant with surrounding rocks. Sills often crop out over a wide area and therefore have a significant impact on landscape and scenery. Because the *igneous rocks* that form sills are usually more resistant than the surrounding rock, sills often form prominent relief features such as scarps and cliffs.

147

■ *e.g.* the dolerite cliffs of High Cup Nick in the northern Pennines, formed by an outcrop of the Great Whin Sill.

skewed frequency distribution: asymmetrical frequency distribution of values around the mean.

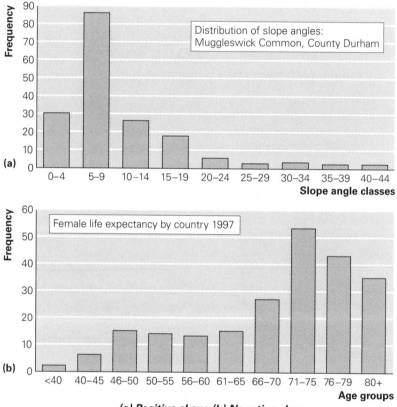

(a) Positive skew; (b) Negative skew

■ Data may have a positive skew (where the tail of the distribution extends to the right) or a negative skew (where the tail extends to the left). Most geographical data show some degree of skewness.

■ *e.g.* Shingle in a river channel has a positive skew (i.e. small particles are more frequent than large particles). Slope angles in a glaciated upland region are often negatively skewed, with steeper slope elements predominating.

■ *TIP* Before applying a statistical test to a data set, you should plot its frequency distribution. If the data approximate a *normal frequency distribution*, you can use any statistical test. However, where the data are skewed, only non-parametric tests such as Spearman rank correlation, the *U-test* and the H-test should be used. You should only use parametric tests (e.g. Pearson product moment, t-test, analysis of variance) on skewed data if you first transform the data (e.g. by taking the logarithms of the original values) to a normal frequency distribution.

slack: linear depression between coastal dune ridges, where the *water table* is at or near the surface.

■ In contrast to sand *dunes*, where the pioneer vegetation (see *pioneer community*) is adapted to drought, dune slacks are dominated by aquatic plants such as flag iris, reeds and rushes.

slope-over-wall cliff (also called 'bevelled cliff'): cliff with a profile comprising a long upper convex slope and a short vertical lower section.

■ The convex slope element is the result of *sub-aerial processes* such as surface wash, *soil creep* and *solifluction*. Only the short vertical section results from wave *erosion*.

■ *e.g.* Many cliffs on the south coasts of Devon and Cornwall have slope-over-wall profiles.

slumping: see *landslide*.

small manufacturing enterprise (SME): private manufacturing firm employing few workers and with a relatively small turnover.

■ Many SMEs are recent start-ups and most occupy positions near the beginning of the production chain, making components or specialising in niche products. SMEs are the 'seedbed' from which a few large, successful companies develop. *External economies* are particularly important to SMEs and encourage clustering.

■ *e.g.* clusters of SMEs specialising in mature products such as textiles, ceramics and fashion wear in Emilia-Romagna in northern Italy.

SME: see *small manufacturing enterprise*.

smog: either a mixture of smoke (and other particulates) and *fog*, or car exhaust gases and other pollutants in the atmosphere of large towns and cities, which restrict visibility.

■ Pollution controls and the switch from coal to cleaner fuels are largely responsible for the disappearance of particulate smogs in MEDCs. However, this type of smog continues to pollute urban areas in countries that retain a coal-based economy (e.g. China, India). Photochemical smog is more widespread today. Formed by car exhaust gases (e.g. nitrogen oxide and hydrocarbons), and the reaction of these gases with sunlight to produce ozone, photochemical smog is a health risk to asthma sufferers and people with other breathing difficulties.

■ *e.g.* Los Angeles is badly affected by photochemical smog. Factors that contribute to the smog problem there include the high levels of car ownership, the sunny climate of southern California and frequent temperature inversions that hinder the dispersal of pollutants.

smokestack industry: heavy processing industry, often polluting and based on low technology.

■ Smokestack industries such as iron and steel, heavy engineering and shipbuilding have undergone steep decline in most MEDCs in the last 50 years. NICs and LEDCs increasingly have a *comparative advantage* in these manufacturing sectors. Deindustrialisation in the 1970s and 1980s hit regions that were

—

overdependent on smokestack industries (e.g. the Great Lakes and northeast USA — the 'rust belt') particularly hard.

SMPs: see *shoreline management plans*.

social exclusion: lack of access to good jobs and a meaningful place in society suffered by many low-income groups owing to long-term unemployment, limited skills, poor educational attainment, prejudice etc.

soil creep: slow downhill movement of soil particles under gravity on a slope as a result of heave processes.

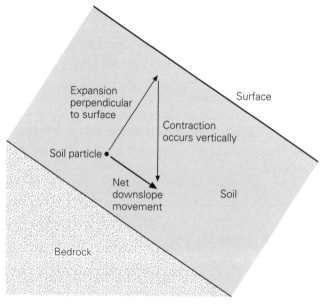

The heave mechanism of soil creep

■ Soil creep is a type of *mass movement*. Wetting or freezing of the soil causes expansion, pushing soil particles perpendicularly towards the surface. On drying or melting, the particles move vertically back to their original level. The effect of this alternate perpendicular and vertical motion is a gradual downslope movement of soil particles.

■ *TIP* You should know that terracettes are visual evidence of soil creep and that soil creep is primarily responsible for the upper convexity of slope profiles in humid temperate environments.

soil erosion: net loss of soil to erosion by wind and runoff.

■ Soil erosion is widespread in both LEDCs and MEDCs. It results from a variety of poor management practices: overcultivation exhausting soil fertility, overgrazing, deforestation, leaving arable land without a protective crop cover etc. Erosion can be reduced by soil conservation measures such as contour ploughing, terracing, mulching, afforestation, planting hedges and windbreaks.

■ *e.g.* Loess soils in China's Yellow River basin lose up to 100 tonnes of soil per hectare annually.

soil profile: vertical section through a soil from the surface to the underlying *parent material*.

■ Most soil profiles comprise a series of layers (recognised by their colour, texture, chemical composition, humus context, etc.) or horizons. The characteristics of the profile and its distinctive horizons are the basis for classifying soils into different types.

soil structure: see *ped*.

soil texture: size of mineral particles in the soil.

■ Soil mineral particles range from fine (clay) to medium (silt) to coarse (sand). *Parent material* determines soil texture (e.g. granite produces sandy soils; shale produces clayey soils) and texture has a strong influence on soil drainage.

■ *TIP* Texture is a physical property of soils. Unlike some other soil characteristics, it is fixed and cannot be modified by farmers.

solifluction: slow flow of fine, water-saturated *regolith* from higher to lower ground (see *gelifluction*).

■ Solifluction is a *mass movement* process, similar to gelifluction except that it occurs outside *periglacial* areas and is not associated with *permafrost*. Solifluction is still active in Britain's uplands and is the cause of extensive solifluction sheets, lobes, stone-banked and earth-banked terraces etc. Large boulders known as ploughing blocks can be rafted slowly downslope by solifluction flows.

solution: *chemical weathering* process by which minerals are dissolved.

■ The solubility of minerals is an important factor in rates of chemical weathering. *Carbonation* is a particular type of solution that dissolves limestone.

solution load: see *load*.

spatial margin of profitability: geographical limits to the profitability of a firm.

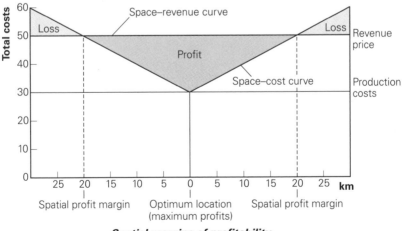

Spatial margins of profitability

■ The theory of spatial margins suggests that firms must locate somewhere within the spatial margins of profitability. However, the exact location is unlikely to be the site of maximum profit. This is because decision-makers have bounded knowledge and their behaviour is satisficing rather than optimising (see *satisficer* and *optimiser*). Exceptionally, a firm may locate outside the spatial profit margins. This may happen with (a) government subsidies or (b) when a firm is willing to tolerate a short-term loss in order to compete in a market.

■ *TIP* The spatial profit margin model is an advance on classical industrial location models which assume that a firm should locate at the point of either maximum profit or minimum cost.

sphere of influence: see *trade area.*

spheroidal weathering: sub-surface *chemical weathering* processes whose effect is to produce rocks and boulders with rounded forms.

■ Chemical weathering attacks the edges and angular corners of sub-surface rocks and boulders. The rounded rocks and boulders are known as corestones. Spheroidal weathering is most evident in the humid tropics and on granitic rocks.

■ *TIP* Despite its name, spheroidal weathering is not a process in itself. Like granular disintegration, spheroidal weathering describes the outcome of chemical weathering processes.

spit: long, narrow *beach* joined to the mainland only at one end.

■ Spits usually develop by *longshore drift* (i.e. they are drift-aligned) across an *estuary* or where the coastline changes direction abruptly. *Recurved laterals* and shingle ridges provide evidence of growth by longshore drift. Spits are joined to the mainland at their proximal end. Their distal ends often have pronounced recurves or hooks which are the result of wave *refraction*. The distribution of spits in the UK corresponds to coasts with low tidal ranges (i.e. less than 2 m).

■ *e.g.* Spurn Point at the mouth of the Humber Estuary, formed by a north–south movement of sand and shingle along the Holderness coast.

spring-line settlement: villages that develop along the line of springs often found at the scarp foot of a cuesta.

■ Spring-line villages occupy wet-point sites (at the junction of permeable and impermeable rocks) where a permanent source of water is available. Spring-lines were attractive sites for rural settlements in regions where surface water was scarce.

■ *TIP* Springs in areas where there is little surface drainage (e.g. chalklands of southern England) are a major cause of *nucleated settlement patterns.*

stability: atmospheric condition where an air parcel displaced from its original level returns to the same level (see *instability*).

■ In stable conditions, there is no tendency for air to rise freely through the atmosphere. Thus cumulus clouds are absent and significant *precipitation* is unlikely. An air parcel is stable because it is cooler and therefore denser and heavier than the surrounding atmosphere.

stack: steep-sided rocky islet located offshore from a cliffed coast.

■ Stacks represent a stage in the destruction of cliffs by marine *erosion*. Many form from the collapse of arches. Eventually stacks are reduced to stumps, and finally they become part of a level *shore platform*.

■ *e.g.* Old Harry Rocks, Dorset.

stadial: comparatively short cold spell that brings a return to glacial conditions.

■ Stadials probably support Alpine glaciation in the uplands, with ice confined to *cirques* and *glacial troughs*.

■ *e.g.* the Loch Lomond stadial between 11,000 and 10,000 BP, when valley *glaciers* re-formed in the Scottish Highlands, the Lake District and north Wales.

■ *TIP* The Devensian glacial was not a period of uniform cold. It was probably interrupted many times by short-lived warmer periods (*inter-stadials*) and brief stadials.

stalactite: a slender finger of calcium carbonate (calcite) that hangs from the roof of a limestone cave.

■ Stalactites are the result of the *precipitation* of calcite from *solution*. Water seeps through the joints of limestone, dissolving the rock by the process of *carbonation*. Droplets of water appear on the roofs of caves and diffuse carbon dioxide to the atmosphere. The solution becomes saturated and precipitation occurs as tiny deposits of calcite. Over thousands of years these deposits build to form stalactites.

stalagmite: stubby pillar-like growth of calcite on the floor of a limestone cave.

■ Stalagmites have a similar origin to *stalactites*. The difference in form is explained by *precipitation* of calcite occurring as water droplets impact on the cave floor.

■ *TIP* The collective name for stalactites and stalagmites is speleothems.

start-up: new small business enterprise that starts from scratch.

stemflow: flow of water along the branches and stems of trees and other plants to the ground.

■ Stemflow usually occurs only after heavy rain. In deciduous woodland, it occurs most often in winter, when interception is low.

storm beach: cobbles and boulders that accumulate near the strandline just above the high water mark.

■ In storm conditions, waves throw coarse sediment to the back of the beach. These sediments cannot be returned seawards because (a) they are too heavy and (b) they are beyond the reach of the *backwash*.

■ *TIP* Note and consider the likely difference between the gradient of a storm beach and the beach below the high water mark.

stratified sampling: objective sampling procedure that divides a *population* into sub-sets, and selects items or individuals from each one.

■ Stratified sampling is used where a statistical population is non-uniform. The sub-sets within the population having been recognised, items or individuals are selected from them either randomly or systematically.

■ *e.g.* A study compares the average size of scree particles on a granite and Carboniferous limestone *scree slope*. Because the size of scree particles is influenced by their position on the slope, each scree slope is divided into three sub-sets — upper, middle and lower. Thirty particles are then selected at random from each sub-set.

■ *TIP* Depending on how the samples are chosen, stratified sampling may be either *random* or *systematic*.

stratus cloud: clouds lying in a level sheet.

■ Stratus clouds have no great vertical development and produce only small amounts of *precipitation*. They are formed by cooling through contact with the Earth's surface, often in stable atmospheric conditions.

■ *TIP* It is a common misconception that clouds form only in unstable conditions. *Anticyclones* cause stable conditions, but often produce masses of stratus cloud. Under a slow-moving 'high', stratus clouds may blot out the sun for several days — a weather phenomenon known as 'anticyclonic gloom'.

stream resurgence: emergence of a stream at the surface after following an underground course.

■ Stream resurgence is a common feature in *karst* scenery. Resurgence may occur (a) where the *water table* reaches the surface; (b) at the interface between permeable limestone and the underlying impermeable rock.

■ *e.g.* Malham Beck stream resurgence, at the foot of Malham Cove in North Yorkshire.

striation: scratch on a rock caused by glacial *abrasion*.

■ Striae are important evidence of the direction of ice movement.

strike-slip fault: see *tear fault*.

sub-aerial processes: processes of *weathering* and *mass movement*.

sub-climax: type of vegetation that has reached the final stage of succession, but where a local environmental factor prevents the development of a true climatic climax community (see *climax vegetation*).

■ *e.g.* Scots pine woodland on the sandy *podzol* soils of the Breckland in Norfolk. The infertile soils prevent the emergence of oak woodland, the climatic climax vegetation of southern England.

subduction zone: destructive plate margin where an oceanic plate slowly descends into the *mantle* and is destroyed.

■ Tectonic plates form at *mid-ocean ridges* and are destroyed at subduction zones. Subduction is often a violent process, and is associated with *earthquakes* and volcanism. *Island arcs, ocean trenches* and fold mountains owe their development to subduction.

■ *e.g.* The Juan de Fuca plate, subducted off the Pacific coast of the northwest USA, is responsible for *volcanoes* such as Mount St Helens and Mount Hood in the Cascade range.

■ *TIP* Because the Earth is not increasing in size, the rate at which new crust forms at mid-ocean ridges must equal the rate of destruction in subduction zones. Yet *plate tectonics* does not give all the answers. For instance, there are no subduction zones in the Atlantic Ocean off the coasts of Europe, North America, Africa and South America.

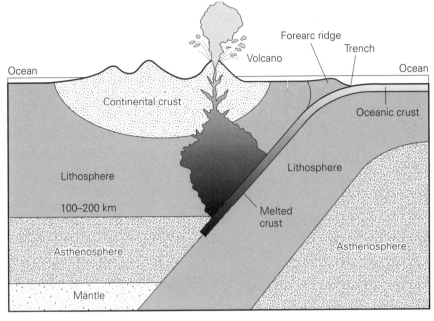

Subduction zone

subsistence agriculture: farming system in which the production of food for household consumption is the priority.

▪ Subsistence farming is confined to LEDCs. However, total self-sufficiency is rare. Most farmers grow some crops for either exchange or cash.

▪ *TIP* Subsistence farming depends on low technology and its yields are often poor. Although in economic terms subsistence farming does not perform well from an ecological perspective, traditional subsistence farming achieves a successful balance with the environment and is sustainable.

suburbanisation: growth of suburbs through the decentralisation of population, industry and commercial activities.

▪ Suburbanisation was made possible by improvements in urban transport systems (e.g. suburban railways and electric tramcars in the late nineteenth century; buses and private motor cars in the twentieth century). Suburbanisation has been responsible for *urban sprawl* and the growth of commuting. In the USA, 'white flight' to the suburbs has contributed to the decay of inner urban areas and the 'ghettoisation' of ethnic minorities and low-income groups.

▪ *TIP* You should recognise the growing trend towards *reurbanisation* in cities in MEDCs. Problems of traffic congestion and the attraction of leisure facilities in the *central business district* have fuelled this trend.

surfing breaker (also called 'spilling breaker'): high-energy wave.

▪ Surfing breakers are high and steep and have short wavelengths. They bring large amounts of energy on to the coast, causing *erosion*; and they transport large volumes of sand and shingle offshore. The effect of these sediment movements is to flatten beaches and create *breakpoint bars*.

■ *TIP* Surfing breakers can occur at any time of year, though they are more frequent in winter. It is an oversimplification to regard the winter profile of beaches as flat and the summer profile as steep.

surging breaker: low-energy wave.

■ Surging breakers are low and have relatively long wavelengths. They transport sand and shingle onshore and form steep beaches with well-developed *berms* and beach faces.

suspended load: see *load*.

sustainability: use of resources to meet current demand without compromising the ability of future generations to meet their own needs.

■ The concept of sustainability is applied to a wide range of economic activities (e.g. tourism, agriculture), economic systems (e.g. urban transport) and environments (urban and rural), at scales ranging from global to local.

swallow hole (also called 'swallet'): vertical or nearly vertical shaft in *karst* (Carboniferous limestone) areas where a surface stream disappears underground.

■ Swallow holes are located close to the geological boundary between limestone and an impermeable rock which supports surface runoff. They are formed by *solution* along a master *joint*. Streams normally disappear within a few hundred metres of flowing on to the limestone.

■ *e.g.* Gaping Ghyll, a 100m vertical shaft on the flanks of Ingleborough, where Fell Beck disappears underground.

swash: movement of water up a beach following a breaking wave.

■ The relative strength of the swash and *backwash* determines the net movement of beach sediment in the inshore zone. Where the swash is more powerful than the backwash, there is a net onshore transport of sediment that steepens beaches. When the backwash is more powerful than the swash, sediments move offshore, reducing beach gradients.

■ *TIP* Measurements of swash and backwash and their relationship to the beach face gradient are meaningful only when undertaken near the high water mark on an ebb tide.

swash alignment: waves that are fully refracted and break parallel to the shoreline (see *refraction*).

■ Swash alignment produces beaches that are crescent-shaped in planform. The paths of swash and backwash are the same and there is no lateral migration of beach sediments (see *longshore drift*).

syncline: symmetrical basin-like geological structure produced by compressive forces in the crust which cause downfolding (see *folding*).

■ *e.g.* the London Basin.

synoptic chart: summary chart that shows weather conditions at a specific time.

■ Synoptic charts show *isobars* and weather *fronts*, and at a number of weather

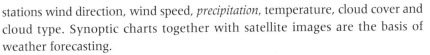

stations wind direction, wind speed, *precipitation*, temperature, cloud cover and cloud type. Synoptic charts together with satellite images are the basis of weather forecasting.

■ *TIP* To interpret weather patterns and make forecasts from weather charts, you must be able to (a) recognise *depressions* (and their associated fronts) and anticyclones; and (b) determine wind directions and from this infer the type of *airmass* affecting an area.

system: group of objects and the relationships between them.

■ The relationships within a system (e.g. flows of energy, money, materials, people) bind the system together and cause it to function as a coherent whole. This is a quality known as holisticity. Systems also have self-adjusting mechanisms or *negative feedback* loops that respond to change and restore balance.

systematic sampling: objective sampling strategy that selects items or individuals from a *population* at regular intervals.

■ Systematic sampling is a simpler alternative to *random sampling*. Instead of generating a random number to select each item or individual, a single number (*n*) is chosen randomly, and every *n*th individual is then selected.

■ *e.g.* In street interviews, every *n*th person passing a researcher might be approached. In a transect across a salt marsh, the vegetation might be measured every *n* metres.

■ *TIP* Although systematic sampling is easier to apply than random sampling, it can give inaccurate results where there is an underlying regularity in the population (e.g. systematic sampling of sand *dunes* where there is a regular spatial pattern of parallel ridges and slacks).

tafoni: weathering hollows up to several metres wide, formed on steep granite surfaces.

talik: pocket of unfrozen water in the *permafrost* layer which may survive for long periods.

talus: alternative name for *scree*.

tear fault (also called 'strike-slip fault'): type of fault where movement along the fault line is lateral, rather than vertical (see *faulting*).

■ *e.g.* the Great Glen that separates Scotland's northwest Highlands from the Grampians.

temperature inversion: increase of temperature with altitude.

■ In the *troposphere*, temperatures normally decrease with altitude (i.e. there is a temperature *lapse*). Temperature inversions occur when: (a) cold air drains from higher slopes into a valley at night, displacing warmer air; (b) air cools through contact with the cold ground surface during *anticyclonic* conditions in winter. Inversions often give rise to *fog* and low *stratus cloud*. The temperature inversion in the stratosphere is due to the concentration of ozone in this part of the atmosphere and its absorption of ultra-violet radiation.

terminal moraine: moraine deposited at the down-valley end of a *glacier* (see *moraine*).

tertiarisation: rapid growth of service activities in the economies of MEDCs in the last 30 or 40 years.

■ Service activities have greatly increased their share of employment and output in MEDCs. The reasons for tertiarisation are complex. They include the decline of employment in other sectors such as manufacturing and agriculture. But just as important are rising disposable incomes, which allow people to satisfy their demand for more services.

■ *e.g.* Tourism has made a huge contribution to the tertiarisation of the economies of MEDCs. Today tourism employs nearly 10% of the UK's workforce.

■ *TIP* The growth of the service sector is not confined to MEDCs. Tertiarisation has occurred in LEDCs. Most self-employment in LEDCs is in the informal service sector, reflecting the shortage of jobs in the formal sector. Some LEDCs have also benefited from the rapid growth of international tourism since 1980.

tertiary sector: generally, an alternative name for all service activities; or, more specifically, those service activities closely linked with industry.

■ *e.g.* the specific definition of the tertiary sector includes services such as transport, communications and utilities such as electricity, gas and water. This definition recognises two other branches of the service sector: *quaternary* and *quinary*.

■ *TIP* The three sub-divisions of the service sector are variously defined. In this book we distinguish: (a) services provided to industry (tertiary); (b) producer-oriented services (quaternary); (c) consumer-oriented services (quinary). Even this classification is far from ideal. For instance, legal services can be provided to a manufacturing firm as well as to private individuals.

thalweg: line of maximum depth (and fastest flow) along a river channel.

■ Even in straight channels, the thalweg is sinuous. This sinuosity, the result of frictional resistance between the channel and water flow, initiates *meander* development.

thermokarst: landscape of surface depressions and thaw lakes in *periglacial environments*, formed by subsidence due to melting ground ice.

■ Thermokarst gets its name because its subsidence depressions resemble *dolines* in *karst* landscapes.

threshold: minimum number of people or the minimum expenditure required to support a good or service in a *central place*.

■ The threshold concept explains the number and range of goods and services supplied by a central place. These functions reflect the level of demand from the population of the central place and its surrounding *trade area*.

■ *e.g.* Services such as pubs and post offices have low thresholds and can be found in the smallest central places. Higher-order services such as department stores and concert halls have very large thresholds. Thus they are confined to the highest-order central places.

■ *TIP* You should make the connection between the concepts of threshold and *hierarchy*.

throughfall: rainfall, initially intercepted by foliage, stems and branches, which drips to the ground.

■ Throughfall becomes increasingly important in the course of a rainfall event. At the start of the event, *interception* is high. Eventually the vegetation's interception storage capacity is reached. Then rates of throughfall and rainfall are roughly equal.

throughflow: lateral movement of water through the soil to streams and rivers.

■ Throughflow slows down the movement of water to streams and rivers and is partly responsible for the *lag time* between maximum *precipitation* and maximum discharge. The speed of throughflow depends on slope, the nature of the parent rock, soil texture and the frequency of pipes (burrows, voids created by old tree roots etc.) in the soil.

thrust fault: see *nappe*.

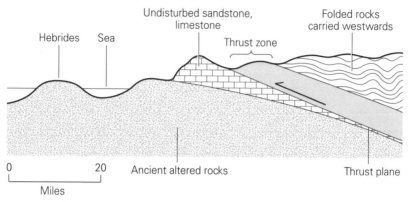

The Moine Thrust: a thrust fault in northwest Scotland

tidal range: difference between the mean high water mark and the mean low water mark along a coastline.

▣ Around the coast of the British Isles, the tidal range varies from under 2 m to over 8 m. The greatest tidal ranges are found in estuaries such as the Severn, where the gradual narrowing of the river mouth increases the amplitude of the tidal wave.

▣ *TIP* You should know that the tidal range has a significant influence on the distribution of coastal depositional landforms. Coasts dominated by tidal landforms (e.g. *mudflats* and *salt marshes*) have high tidal ranges; those with *spits, tombolos* and similar landforms are generally confined to coasts with a low tidal range.

tidewater industry: industry located on the coast to give access to sea transport.

▣ Tidewater industries usually locate close to deepwater terminals to take advantage of cheap transport offered by very large bulk-carrying and container ships. Low-value materials such as mineral ores can be imported in bulk, and manufactured products can be exported and distributed by sea. Tidewater sites are often least-transport-cost locations (see *Weber's theory*).

▣ *e.g.* the iron and steel industry at Port Talbot, which imports iron ore, coal and limestone in bulk, and can export steel directly by sea to international markets.

▣ *TIP* Remember that apart from cheap sea transport, tidewater locations offer other advantages (e.g. extensive areas of reclaimed land for huge industrial complexes such as oil refining and petrochemicals; water for cooling and effluent disposal; remoteness from residential suburbs, avoiding pollution).

TNC: see *transnational corporation*.

tombolo: *beach* that joins an island to the mainland.

▣ Tombolos may be either swash-aligned (see *swash alignment*) or drift-aligned (see *longshore drift*) features.

▣ *e.g.* Chesil Beach, Dorset, which joins the Isle of Portland to the mainland, and is swash-aligned.

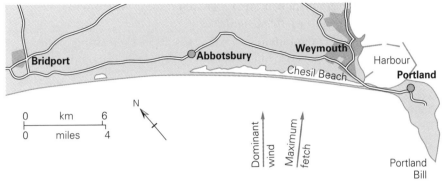

Chesil Beach, west Dorset: a swash-aligned tombolo

■ *TIP* Tombolos, together with other beach forms (e.g. *spits, barrier beaches*) are classified by their shape, not their origin. This is not entirely satisfactory: it means that two beaches with quite different origins might have the same name.

topological map: idealised transport network map that transforms places to points and routes to straight lines.

■ Topological maps allow quantitative description of transport networks in terms of their *connectivity* and the accessibility of places.

■ *e.g.* the map of the London underground network.

■ *TIP* Remember that topological maps transform geographical space so that the precise location of places and the actual path of routes bear little resemblance to reality. For a user of the London underground, this information is irrelevant. The London underground map simplifies the network, making it easy to use.

tor: small rocky outcrop with prominent vertical and horizontal *joints*, found in exposed positions on hilltops and valley sides in areas of granite or coarse sandstone.

■ Tors are thought to result from sub-surface *chemical weathering*. Weathering processes such as *hydrolysis* are concentrated where the vertical joints occur most frequently. The rock in these areas rots and is removed by erosional processes. Tors are the massively jointed areas of rock that resisted weathering.

■ *e.g.* granite tors on the summit of Beinn Mheadhoin in the Cairngorms.

trade area (also called 'sphere of influence' and 'hinterland'): area served with goods and services by a central place (see *central place theory, centrality* and *Reilly's model*).

■ Trade areas vary in size according to the status of a central place (i.e. its centrality), its accessibility, its population density and the purchasing power of the population. Idealised trade areas in central place theory form interlocking networks of hexagons, with smaller trade areas 'nested' inside larger ones.

■ *TIP* In reality, central places do not have clearly defined trade areas. Each function provided by a central place has its own unique trade area. Nor is such a trade area delimited by a simple boundary. Trade areas of competing centres overlap, with the intensity of a trade area diminishing with distance from a central place (see *Huff's interaction model*).

transgression: eustatic rise in sea level which results in a retreating coastline.

■ Transgressions are responsible for submerged coastlines and landforms such as *rias*, *fjords* and *estuaries*.

■ *e.g.* the Flandrian transgression — the worldwide rise in sea level between 20,000 and 6,000 BP that followed the melting of Devensian ice.

■ *TIP* You should realise that during a *glacial*, sea level falls and the coastline advances. This phenomenon, the opposite of transgression, is known as a regression.

transnational corporation (TNC): very large company with factories and offices in more than one country, and which markets products and services worldwide.

■ TNCs have been the driving force behind the *globalisation* of the world economy in the past 30 years. Two-thirds of all world trade takes place either between or within TNCs.

■ *e.g.* the Ford Motor Company, which has assembly plants in six continents.

■ *TIP* TNCs are controversial. Their activities and strategies bring both benefits and disbenefits. You should understand the impact of TNCs on national and regional economies, and clarify your own views on the various issues and outcomes.

transpiration: *evaporation* of moisture from the pores (stomata) of plants.

■ In many terrestrial *ecosystems*, the output of moisture from transpiration exceeds evaporation from the ground surface.

■ *TIP* *Precipitation* intercepted by plants and evaporated is not included in transpiration. The combined output of evaporation and transpiration is *evapo-transpiration*.

trophic level: different feeding levels within a *food chain* or *food web*.

■ Organisms in a food web or food chain can be grouped into a series of discrete trophic levels. The first trophic level comprises primary producers (green plants) or autotrophs. Primary consumers (2nd level) are herbivores that feed directly on plants. Secondary and tertiary consumers (3rd and 4th levels) are carnivores and omnivores. Decomposers operate at all trophic levels. The relative loss of energy due to respiration increases at higher trophic levels. This causes a decrease in the *biomass* at each trophic level.

tropopause: boundary between the *troposphere* and the stratosphere.

troposphere: lowest layer of the atmosphere, extending from the Earth's surface to an average height of 11 km.

■ The troposphere contains most of the gases and nearly all of the clouds, *precipitation* and vertical winds in the atmosphere. The troposphere is defined by its *lapse rate*.

trough head: steep rock wall that marks the up-valley end of a *glacial trough* or U-shaped valley.

▨ Trough heads form where *glacier* ice from an extensive icefield converges, increasing the speed of the glacier and its powers of *erosion*.

truncated spur: pre-glacial spur that projected into a valley and has been planed off by glacial *erosion*.

tsunami: large wave at sea, generated by an *earthquake* or a submarine *landslide*.

▨ Tsunamis travel at speeds of 700 kph. In the open ocean, they are usually less than a metre high. In shallow coastal waters, tsunamis increase dramatically in height (15 m or more) and are highly destructive.

▨ *e.g.* the tsunami that struck Hilo (Hawaii) in May 1960, killing 61 people and causing damage to property of over $20 million.

tufa: calcium carbonate (calcite) deposits precipitated from *solution*.

▨ Tufa forms *stalactites* and *stalagmites* in caves. Extensive tufa deposits also form around *waterfalls* and springs in limestone areas.

tundra: treeless vegetation zone in the sub-arctic and in high mountains, dominated by low-growing lichens, mosses, sedges, herbs and woody plants.

▨ Plant growth in the tundra is limited by the short growing season, severe winter temperatures and exposure. Most plants are perennials, and many show adaptations to climate such as leaf rosettes, cushions and a low-growing habit. Net primary *productivity* and *biodiversity* are low in the tundra.

▨ *TIP* Although average annual productivity is low, during the summer when daylight may last for 24 hours, growth rates are relatively high. Seasonal migrations of birds and mammals also occur in the spring to take advantage of an abundance of food (insects, herbs, berries etc.) during the brief summer.

turbulent flow: chaotic flow of water in eddies and vortices in stream channels.

▨ Turbulent flow results from the friction between the channel bed and banks and water in the channel. Irregular upland channels, with steep gradients and coarse *bedloads*, typically have turbulent flow. Turbulent flow produces localised high velocities, which give upland streams the power to transport their coarse bedload.

ubac slope: slope facing away from the sun (see *aspect*).

▓ *e.g.* a north-facing slope in the British Isles.

UDC: see *urban development corporation*.

undernutrition: condition caused by too little food intake, which ultimately leads to death by starvation.

▓ The Food & Agriculture Organisation (FAO) identifies undernutrition among people who do not consume enough food to maintain their body weight.

▓ *TIP* Make sure that you understand the difference between undernutrition and *malnutrition*. Most dietary problems in LEDCs relate to malnutrition rather than undernutrition.

underpopulation: situation where an increase in the population of an area would improve the population/resource ratio and standards of living (see *overpopulation* and *optimum population*).

understorey: layer of vegetation in a forest *ecosystem* immediately below the canopy.

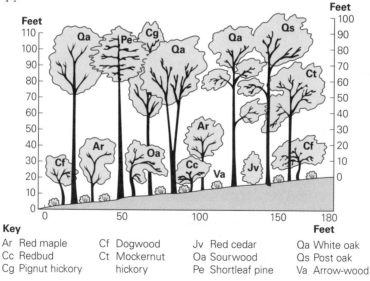

Key

Ar Red maple	Cf Dogwood	Jv Red cedar	Qa White oak
Cc Redbud	Ct Mockernut	Oa Sourwood	Qs Post oak
Cg Pignut hickory	hickory	Pe Shortleaf pine	Va Arrow-wood

Temperate deciduous forest, North Carolina: canopy and understorey

■ *e.g.* In the temperate deciduous forest, small trees and shrubs such as hazel, holly and elder form an understorey below the canopy of dominant oaks.

unit labour costs: cost of wages etc. paid to a workforce compared to output and productivity.

■ Unit labour costs show that paying high wages can be cost-effective if output and productivity are high. For this reason, a location in an LEDC where wages are only a fraction of those in MEDCs may not be advantageous if productivity is low.

■ *e.g.* Southeast England has the highest labour costs in the UK, but the lowest unit labour costs. Northern Ireland has the lowest labour costs, but one of the highest unit labour costs. Thus it makes sense, *ceteris paribus*, for some firms to locate in the southeast rather than Northern Ireland, even though labour costs in the southeast are much higher.

urban development corporation (UDC): government-appointed quango whose brief was to regenerate run-down and derelict areas in major British cities.

■ UDCs were given some government money to clear land, assemble sites and build new roads in inner-city areas. Following this initial government sponsorship, they were expected to attract the bulk of investment from the private sector. UDCs were given powers to tackle the problems of their areas directly and were able to by-pass local planning authorities. All the UDCs were wound up by the late 1990s.

■ *e.g.* London Docklands, which was the first and most successful UDC and included the development of Canary Wharf and the Docklands' Light Railway.

■ *TIP* You need to assess the success of UDCs and their contribution towards urban regeneration in the 1980s and 1990s.

urban growth: absolute increase in population living in urban areas or the physical expansion of urban areas.

urbanisation: increase in the proportion of a population living in urban areas.

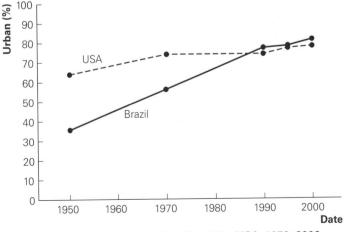

Urbanisation in Brazil and the USA, 1950–2000

■ Urbanisation is currently occurring in most LEDCs. It is the result of (a) rural–urban *migration* and (b) lower levels of *mortality* in urban areas compared to the countryside.

■ *e.g.* Brazil's level of urbanisation increased from 36% in 1950 to 81% in 2000.

■ *TIP* Urbanisation does not necessarily accompany *urban growth* (the rural population may be growing faster than the urban population). You need to be quite clear that urbanisation and urban growth describe different processes.

urbanisation diseconomies: economic disadvantages of locating in large urban areas.

■ Urbanisation diseconomies include the higher labour costs, greater traffic congestion, higher land values and rents, more unionised workforce etc. of large urban areas compared to smaller urban areas and rural areas. These diseconomies have provided a major stimulus to the decentralisation of economic activities in MEDCs in the past 50 years.

urbanisation economies: advantages to firms of locating in urban areas where essential economic and social infrastructures are already in place.

■ Firms locating in urban areas incur only a fraction of the cost of providing essential infrastructures such as housing for workers, schools, roads, electricity and gas grids, and water supply. In the nineteenth century, some industrialists built canals, roads and small towns to serve their factories and accommodate their workers.

urban land-use models: see *Burgess, Hoyt, Harris–Ullman* and *Mann* models.

urban–rural manufacturing shift: increase in the proportion of manufacturing in small towns and rural areas in MEDCs since 1970.

■ Conurbations and large towns and cities have experienced a massive decline in their manufacturing base in the past 30 years. This contrasts with small towns and rural areas, which have seen a modest increase in manufacturing during this period. The principal reason for this urban–rural shift has been the acute shortage of suitable sites for modern factories in large urban areas.

■ *TIP* The urban–rural shift is not about the relocation of factories. It is about factories closing in large urban areas (especially inner-city areas) and not being replaced by new ones. Meanwhile, a disproportionate amount of new industrial investment has gone to small towns and rural areas.

urban sprawl: loss of countryside caused by the physical expansion (often unplanned) of towns and cities (see *green belt*).

■ Towns and cities now cover nearly 12% of the area of the UK. The forecast demand for 4.4 million new homes by 2016, many on *greenfield sites*, will result in further erosion of the British countryside.

U-shaped glacial valley: see *glacial trough*.

U-test: statistical test that assesses the significance of the difference between two sets of sample data.

■ The U-test determines the likelihood that two groups of sample data are drawn from the same statistical *population*. It is a non-parametric test that can be used on data that have either *normal* or *skewed frequency distributions*.

■ *e.g.* a comparison of the shape of a *random sample* of 25 particles from a river channel from a downstream site and 25 particles from an upstream site.

■ *TIP* If in doubt, always use a parametric test such as the U-test or the Spearman rank correlation which makes no assumptions about the distribution of the population.

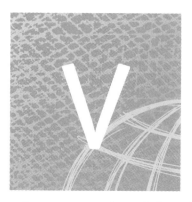

vadose cave: cave formed above the *water table* by subterranean streams in areas of *karst*.

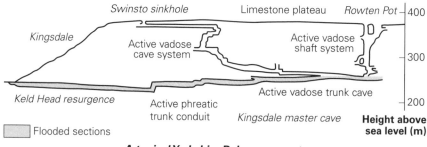

A typical Yorkshire Dales cave system

▓ Vadose caves are often deep, twisting canyons formed by streams cutting into the cave floor.

▓ *TIP* Vadose caves and *phreatic caves* provide important information about fluctuations in the level of the water table in the past.

valley train: infill of coarse *glacio-fluvial deposits* across a flat valley floor.

▓ A valley train is a smaller version of a *sandur* or outwash plain. Meltwater streams spread deposits of sand and gravel across the valley floor. Unlike a sandur, the lateral development of a valley train is limited by the valley sides.

▓ *e.g.* the Markarfljot Valley in Thorsmark, southwest Iceland.

▓ *TIP* Although valley trains are confined to areas of active glaciation, many valleys in northern Britain were filled by valley trains during the last *deglaciation* (8,000–10,000 years ago). In many places, the coarse *outwash* debris is today covered by fine *overbank deposits* of silt and clay.

vauclusian spring: another name for a *stream resurgence*.

vent: roughly circular opening in the Earth's crust where volcanic material reaches the surface.

▓ *TIP* You should note that a fissure is a similar opening, except that it is long and narrow.

vertical integration: type of industrial organisation where most production stages take place within a single firm and on the same site.

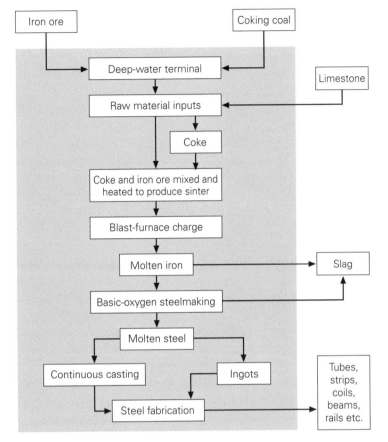

Vertical integration: modern iron and steelworks

■ *e.g.* an integrated iron and steelworks such as Redcar-Lackenby on Teesside.

■ *TIP* Note the alternative production strategy — *horizontal organisation*.

volcanic neck: steep-sided and isolated plug of volcanic rock, which occupied the *vent* of a now extinct *volcano*.

■ The cone of the extinct volcano has been removed by *erosion*; only the resistant rock that once filled the vent survives.

■ *e.g.* the Devil's Tower, Wyoming.

volcano: opening in the Earth's crust, surrounded by a cone of ash and lava, where molten rock and gases reach the surface.

■ Volcanoes fall into two types, depending on the nature of their *ejecta*. Strato-volcanoes (see *magma chamber*) are steep-sided and cone-shaped, and consist of alternate layers of ash and viscous lava. Eruptions from strato-volcanoes are often explosive. Shield volcanoes are broad-based and have gentle slopes, which result from eruptions of fluid *basalt* lavas.

■ *e.g.* Mount St Helen's (Washington state) is a strato-volcano; Mauna Loa (Hawaii) is a shield volcano.

Von Thunen's theory: theory that explains how and why patterns of agricultural land use and land-use intensity vary with distance from a central market.

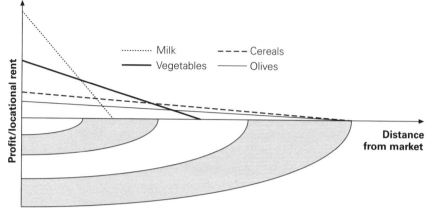

Von Thunen's theory of land use zones around a market

■ According to the theory, land use is determined by the market price for 1 hectare's crop production, minus the cost of transporting the production of 1 hectare to market. As distance from the market increases, transport costs rise and profits fall. Thus each crop has its own profit or bid rent curve. At any given distance from market, the crop yielding the highest profit will be grown. Land-use intensity also varies with distance from market. Fertilisers and labour are available at the market. These are input at lowest cost nearest the market, raising intensity in this zone. Finally, Von Thunen said that perishable products such as soft fruit, vegetables and milk should also locate close to market.

■ *TIP* Von Thunen's theory (1826) has limited relevance to modern agriculture. In particular, the revolution in transport that has occurred since Von Thunen's day has greatly reduced the influence of transport costs. Even so, though it is dated, you should not be overcritical of the theory. Given its simplifying assumptions (e.g. a single market, transport costs proportional to distance and weight, an area of uniform soils and climate, farmers motivated only to maximise their profits), the theory's outcomes (i.e. concentric land-use zones around the market) are entirely logical and consistent. Above all, by isolating the distance factor, the theory provides a valuable insight into the effect of distance on agricultural land-use patterns.

V-shaped valley: steep-sided river valley with a narrow floor.

■ V-shaped valleys owe their cross-sectional shape to rapid incision by a river. Vertical *erosion* exceeds the rates of lateral erosion by the river and the lowering of the valley sides by *sub-aerial processes*. Steep channel gradients and coarse *bedload* assist vertical erosion. V-shaped valleys are most characteristic of upland streams and rivers. Interlocking spurs are found with V-shaped valleys and develop where incision occurs in a meandering channel.

warm front: leading edge of the *warm sector* in a *depression*, where polar air is replaced by tropical air (see *front*).

■ At the warm front, tropical air rises at a shallow angle above the colder, denser polar air. This rising conveyor of warm air is sucked upwards by the warm front jet, producing extensive cloud and prolonged *precipitation*.

■ *TIP* You should understand the link between the processes taking place at the warm front and resultant weather patterns. You should be familiar with the sequence of changes in pressure, temperature, precipitation, cloud, wind direction and visibility that occur at the approach and passage of a warm front.

warm sector: wedge of relatively warm tropical air in a *depression* bounded by the *warm* and *cold fronts*.

■ The warm sector comprises tropical maritime (Tm) air. It is the contrast between this warm tropical air and the colder polar air in a depression that is responsible for the active processes found at the weather fronts.

water balance: relationship between *precipitation*, streamflow, *evapotranspiration*, and soil moisture and groundwater storage in a drainage basin.

■ The water balance equation is:

Precipitation = Streamflow + Evapotranspiration +/– Changes in storage
$$(P) \qquad (Q) \qquad (E) \qquad (S)$$

In terms of streamflow, the water balance equation becomes:

$$Q = P - E +/- S$$

■ *TIP* In order to understand the water balance, consider how seasonal changes in precipitation, evapotranspiration, soil moisture storage and groundwater storage might affect streamflow in the British Isles.

water cycle: continuous movement of water (as liquid water, ice and vapour) between the oceans, continents and *atmosphere*.

■ The water cycle comprises (a) stores (e.g. oceans, *glaciers*, groundwater) and (b) pathways (e.g. *runoff*, *evapotranspiration*) that link these stores together. Storage times vary from around 14 days for water in the atmosphere, to thousands of years for ice in Greenland and Antarctic glaciers. Precipitation is proportionally higher over the continents than over the oceans; and evaporation is proportionally higher over the oceans.

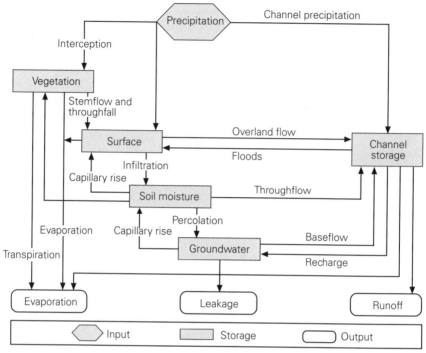

The drainage basin water cycle

▦ *TIP* You should understand how, at the scale of the drainage basin, human activities can modify the water cycle. These modifications may be deliberate (e.g. reservoirs) or unintentional (e.g. land-use changes).

waterfall: rock step in a river's long profile which produces a vertical fall of water.

▦ Waterfalls most often occur where (a) a band of more resistant rock cuts across a river's course; (b) a tributary valley hangs above a *glacial trough*; and (c) a river plunges over the edge of a plateau or an *escarpment*.

▦ *e.g.* Aysgarth Falls, North Yorkshire, where resistant bands of limestone cut across the course of the River Ure.

watershed: boundary of a *drainage basin*.

water table: upper surface of the zone of saturation in a permeable rock.

wave: superficial undulation of a water surface caused by winds blowing across a lake or sea (see *surfing breaker* and *surging breaker*).

▦ Waves consist of orbital movements of water molecules that diminish with depth. Water only begins to show forward movement in waves when they enter shallow water. (In open water, a wave's apparent forward movement is in fact a movement of energy.) The power of waves (square of wave height multiplied by velocity) is determined by three factors: *fetch*, wind speed and wind duration. Waves are the main source of energy that drives the coastal system and are responsible for the development of most coastal landforms. Other sources of energy are tides and the wind.

W

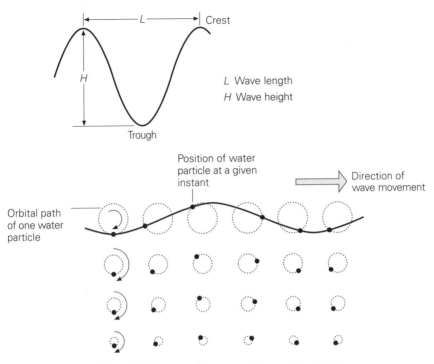

L Wave length
H Wave height

Position of water particle at a given instant

Direction of wave movement

Orbital path of one water particle

The orbital diameter of water particles within a wave and their associated velocities decrease with depth

Wave parameters

wave-cut notch: recess at the base of cliffs caused by the concentrated erosive action of waves around the high water mark.

■ The formation of a wave-cut notch undermines cliffs and ultimately leads to their collapse and recession.

wave-cut platform: see *shore platform.*

wave refraction: see *refraction.*

weather: state of the atmosphere at a given time.

■ Weather describes the day-to-day changes in temperature, *precipitation*, cloud cover, sunshine, wind, pressure etc.

weathering: in situ breakdown of rocks at the Earth's surface and close to the surface, by physical, chemical and biological processes (see *physical weathering* and *chemical weathering*).

■ *TIP* Remember that weathering and *erosion* describe quite different processes. Weathering is the breakdown of rocks exposed to variations in moisture and temperature. Erosion is the wearing away and transport of rocks by the action of rivers, *glaciers*, waves and wind.

Weber's theory: theory that the optimal location for a manufacturing industry is the point of minimum transport cost.

■ Weber's theory (1909) suggested that transport was the primary factor influencing the location of industry and that transport costs were a function of weight and distance. The optimal location is the one that minimises the combined costs of transporting materials to the factory, and transporting the finished good to market. Weber also devised a material index to show in general terms whether an industry would be material or market oriented. The material index is calculated by dividing the weight of raw materials by the weight of the finished product. Where an industry has a material index of more than 1, it should locate at materials; an index of less than 1 indicates a market location.

■ *TIP* The locational influence of transport costs is relatively unimportant for most modern industries. However, for a handful of processing industries (e.g. iron and steel, non-ferrous metal smelting, oil refining, sugar refining) whose raw materials undergo significant weight loss, Weber's ideas remain relevant.

wetted perimeter: total length of a river channel in cross-section which is in contact with the water.

wilderness area: conservation area where there is little or no human interference or management of natural systems.

■ The US National Parks Service is responsible for dozens of wilderness areas. Unlike *National Parks*, national monuments and other conservation areas, there is no attempt to make wilderness areas accessible to the public. Most wilderness areas are remote and in the USA they are mainly confined to Alaska and the Western Cordillera.

■ *e.g.* Glacier Peak Wilderness, Washington state.

wildfire: natural fires caused by lightning strikes.

■ Wildfire is important to the functioning and health of many *ecosystems*. Fire opens up a dense canopy and allows a forest to regenerate. Some pine cones only open and release their seeds in the heat of a fire; and fires burn years of accumulated leaf litter, returning the nutrients to the soil for recycling.

winterbourne: stream in a chalkland area which flows only during the winter months when the *water table* is at the surface.

■ Winterbournes, governed by the height of the water table, usually originate on chalk *escarpments* as *dip slope* springs.

world city: city that functions as a command-and-control centre for the global economy.

■ World cities are the highest-order cities in the global urban hierarchy. They specialise in *producer services* such as finance and banking and are the headquarters of major *transnational corporations*.

■ *e.g.* New York, Tokyo and London are the leading world cities and the only ones that are truly global.

■ *TIP* You should know that world cities play a pivotal role in the *globalisation* of the world economy.

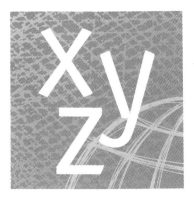

xerophyte: plant adapted to withstand long periods of soil drought.

▥ Xerophytes have developed several strategies for coping with drought. Some annuals — drought evaders — remain dormant as seeds during droughts. They grow, flower and seed only when moisture becomes available. Others have physical adaptations to conserve moisture, store moisture (e.g. succulents) or tap groundwater (e.g. phreatophytes).

xerosere: type of *plant succession* where soil drought is the main limiting factor to the *pioneer* colonising species (see *psammosere* and *lithosere*).

▥ *e.g.* plant succession in the following environments: hot deserts; coastal sand dunes; bare rock surfaces.

▥ *TIP* Remember that shortages of moisture for plant growth are not just caused by low rainfall. In the British Isles, coastal dunes (high porosity) and bare rock surfaces (rapid runoff) are responsible for soil drought.

yardang: streamlined parallel ridge found in tropical deserts, usually less than 10 m high and 100 m or more in length, aligned in the direction of the prevailing wind.

▥ Yardangs usually form in less resistant rocks. Their alignment suggests that the wind has been an important erosive agent in their development.

yield: in agriculture, the tonnage of crop produced per unit area.

▥ Crop yields depend on a number of physical and human factors, including soil fertility, climate, intensity of cultivation and protection against pests and diseases.

▥ *e.g.* The average yield of winter wheat in eastern England is around 7 tonnes per hectare.

zero growth: situation where a population just replaces itself.

▥ Even though population growth may be below the replacement level, zero growth may not be achieved. *Population momentum*, caused by a relatively large proportion of young adults and children, will be responsible for continuing population growth.

▥ *e.g.* Although China's fertility is currently well below replacement level, the momentum of its population means that zero growth will not be achieved until the mid-century.

zeugen: tabular-shaped rock outcrops in hot desert areas, attributed to wind *erosion*.

zonal soil: mature soil whose main characteristics have been determined by climate.

		COOL CLIMATES		WARM CLIMATES
MOIST CLIMATES	**Permafrost soils**	**Tundra soils**		
	Pedalfers	Podzolic	Podzols Brown earths Prairie soils	Yellow and red podzols
		Lateritic		Tropical red soils Lateritic soils
DRY CLIMATES	Pedocals		Chernozems Chestnut brown soils Brown soils Sierozems	Various tropical pedocals

Increasing leaching →

Zonal classification of soils

■ The zonal soil classification recognises broad belts of soil at the global scale which correspond with climate and vegetation. The balance between *precipitation* and *evapotranspiration* is the critical factor in zonal soil development (depth, horizonation, acidity etc.). An excess of precipitation causes *eluviation* and *leaching*. Acidic soils formed in these conditions are known as pedalfers. Where precipitation is less than potential evapotranspiration, minerals such as calcium carbonate accumulate in the *soil profile* and moisture is drawn to the surface by capillary action. This results in a group of alkaline soils or pedocals.

■ *e.g.* podzol (a pedalfer); *chernozem* (a pedocal).

■ *TIP* At a regional or local scale, where climate is fairly uniform, the zonal classification has limited value. Differences in soils at this scale owe more to *parent material* and drainage than to climate.

zone: in urban geography, a concentric ring of uniform land use in a city.

■ *Burgess's zonal model* is based on the idea of zones of land use organised around the city centre. This zonation is explained by the process of invasion and succession. The bid rent model produces a similar zonal land-use pattern (see *bid rent theory*).